THE GUARDIAN CROSSWORD BOOK NO. 1

Also by the same author,
and available in Coronet Books:

The Guardian Crossword Book No. 2
Coronet Quick Crosswords Book 1
Coronet Quick Crosswords Book 2

The Guardian Crossword Book No. 1

Edited by John Perkin

with a foreword by
Paul Jennings

CORONET BOOKS
Hodder and Stoughton

Coronet edition 1969
Sixth impression 1980

Printed and bound in Great Britain for
Hodder and Stoughton Paperbacks, a
division of Hodder and Stoughton Ltd.,
Mill Road, Dunton Green, Sevenoaks,
Kent (Editorial Office: 47 Bedford
Square, London, WC1 3DP) by
Hazell Watson & Viney Ltd.,
Aylesbury, Bucks

ISBN 0 340 04368 7

FOREWORD

A HISPID PROBLEM

It's easy to imagine some literary vision of the future, on the lines of *Erewhon* (where crime is treated as illness and illness as crime) in which crossword addiction is cured in State clinics. There would be planned, gradual withdrawal from this mad, obsessional world where words, although perfectly dead and removed from the rich organic field of speech and literature, are viewed in fetishistic patterns. As a first step, perhaps, patients would be allowed to do crosswords in diagrams which, each day, *were a little less symmetrical* (and it's typical of the whole crossword thing that the diagram doesn't have mirror symmetry, merely a baffling diagonal symmetry; it's the same pattern when you turn it through 180°, but not when you turn it through 90°. As a matter of fact some diagrams do have diagonal mirror symmetry and others don't). Gradually words would be introduced that didn't have to fit in with other vertical or horizontal words at all, for they would be bordered by continuous black squares. Then phrases, then whole sentences. Poetry, beginning at first with tightly-knit acrostic poems like the ones Guinness have used in some of their advertisements, or composed entirely of anagrams or palindromes, would, in an ordered sequence, eventually be free-flowing, untrammelled lyrics. Finally cured, the patients would be unsteady on their linguistic legs at first; they would speak with the unnatural, sharply focussed, literary quality of someone writing fluently in a language not his own, like Nabokov; but they would eventually relax, like other men, absorbed into the normal life-flow of words as the servants of meaning, language, life. . . .

The trouble would be to get anyone to attend, of course.

None of us *wants* to be cured. There is nothing more shame-faced and unconvincing than a crossword addict trying to tell you that the habit has increased his word-power, like those little page-filler items in the *Reader's Digest*. I personally have found an extraordinary thing about words learnt in crosswords; my mind *rejects* them again. I look in the solution the next day and I find that the corner I couldn't do depended on some word like *hispid*, or *banausic*, or *rhopalic*—and three days after that I have forgotten these words again. In any case there simply isn't room in one's mind, life being what it is, for words like *rhopalic* (it is, I discover on looking it up yet again, 'applied to verse in which each word contains one syllable more than the one immediately preceding it'. I don't write that kind of verse, and I've never heard of anyone else who does either).

Moreover, most of us are not so far gone as to care very much for the crossword that has to be done with dictionaries. Anyone, given the time, who has got as far as H*S*I* for one of those take-it-or-leave-it one-word clues, in this case *bristly*, can work alphabetically through the dictionary—HASCID, HASTIC, HESCIL, (with increasing desperation) HESSIM, HESZIT, HISHIC, until he comes to that damn HISPID. But we have our livings to earn, our children to be dandled on our knees, our lives to be lived; we're not as far gone as *that*. We know where to stop.

The *Guardian's* is the one for us. It keeps this *hispid* stuff to a minimum, even though it occasionally expects us to know textile terms like *noil* or *slub*. There is only one remote daily rival, the one in the Other Paper. Both have the magic 15 x 15 spaces. The one in the O.P. is blacker, and a great deal easier to read, and isn't stuffed away inside the paper as the *Guardian's* is. But the great thing about the latter is its constancy. You know where you are with it, it is always roughly of the same standard. It has taken the measure of its solvers. The O.P.'s, on the other hand, is a push-over on some days, all anagrams and quotes from Gray's *Elegy in a Country Churchyard*, and then they suddenly slip in one aimed at some mad vicar, a Senior Wrangler in 1911, and a sometime Classics don, who also taught English to sixth forms to help out during the war; and even he, pottering in his slippers in the beautiful library, with its globe and busts of Cicero and Horace, of the vicarage in some Jane Austen park, looking out on to a falling soft landscape of trees, has to give the whole morning to it.

I suspect that the real reason none of us wants to be cured is that the exactly right crossword—not the push-over, not the mad vicar's—refreshes that part of the human mind (what am I saying? The *whole* of the human mind) which thirsts after order and perfection. The world is full of imponderables that seem to get more imponderable every day—race, the Bomb, drugs, money, strikes, crashes, the Chinese, de Gaulle, money, Vietnam, de Gaulle, race, students, Unhappy Married Women, de Gaulle—and we might end day after day increasingly doubtful of our ability to control and master *anything*, were it not for this little square in which honest effort and basic intelligence—for let's not beat about the bush, not everyone can do them—combine to allow us to do, every day, at least one perfect thing.

Some might say, like the doctors in my imaginary State clinics, that this is to retreat from reality, or at least from what Aquinas calls the practico-practical judgement, to the merely speculative judgement—and speculation of a particularly narrow and determined kind, since for all the wild adventures of HESCIL, HESZIT and the rest, we are (if successful) driven to the one and only, inevitable, HISPID in the end. But I do not agree. I believe that the human capacity for solving, for producing order, must be given *some* exercise or it will wither completely. I believe in crosswords as I believe in the well-made play. After that I (and I believe I speak here for all of us solvers) can match my mere emotions and instincts and passions with the best of them in the adjoining news columns.

It follows from all this (goodness, how the typewriter seems to run on almost of its own accord when one is writing for crossword-solvers; one does not have to say, apologetically, are you with me, do you see the logical steps, to *you*, dear readers!) that we trust our puzzle-setters to combine genuine difficulty with genuine logic. The perfect clue, in fact, is a paradox, for its answer must be blindingly obvious, the only possible one, when we see it, and yet it must be concealed with the utmost cunning. We are willing to accept a few personal conventions, which in any case we soon get to know. Every *Guardian* solver knows that the word *point* in any clue involves the letter N, W,

S or E, a compass point. We accept, especially if we have done all the horizontals involved, that the down clue *Moslem leader said to be virtuous*, M*R*L, must be *moral*, M being the leader or first letter of *Moslem*.

Sometimes we rebel. One of the reasons I and not a better man was asked to write this Introduction was that I wrote an angry letter (for we solvers, we order-imposers, can be passionate, we are whole men) complaining (not because of failure, because I'd *done* it) that the solution to *says a lot for the army, like a TV* producer, was *talkative*. This is of course an anagram of *like a TV*, but I objected to being expected to supply TA for the 'army' part of the clue. Afterwards I looked at it again and thought maybe it *was* just within the bounds of fairness. Meanwhile the *Guardian's* Crossword Editor has written to me, and doesn't mind my revealing, that on reflection he thinks maybe I was right. Passionate and reasonable, that's what we are.

Only one thing worries me. As I have said, we who do the *Guardian* crossword (and I sometimes do the O.P. one as well, on non-mad-vicar days) are a pretty well-organised lot. We know it's an addiction, but we keep it under control, we don't let it run our lives. What are we doing with a whole *book* of the things, then? For there is no doubt that even the best of us could take several days to do all the puzzles in this book, retiring to some secret room, dictionaryless but comfortable, while our families evaded queries about us, knowing we were off on another jag.

No, of course! This book is to sustain us when we have perforce to travel in lands where they either don't have crosswords at all (*mots croisés* aren't the same thing at all; you can no more get a decent crossword in France than a decent cup of tea) or where, as in America, their crosswords are big and simple, instead of hard, dense, subtle, quirky, maddening, surprising, intelligible, challenging, human, witty, awful, and full of divine coincidences, as they ought to be: and as life is.

Paul Jennings

INTRODUCTION

Crosswords are not really so very difficult to solve—they are a good deal more difficult to compose—but solving them often needs a special way of thinking. This is something that can be developed. Anyone who has never done a crossword before and picking one up for the first time may be forgiven for thinking this is something quite beyond him, a code he cannot begin to break. But if he takes a look at the solution the next day and compares the clues he will almost certainly spot the connections, one hopes with delight and surprise. A week studying the 'form' of the daily *Guardian* crosswords and he should be able to have a crack at a virgin puzzle. He probably won't complete it, but even if he only gets a quarter solved he will have found the key to crosswords in general.

We are not concerned here with the sort of prize puzzles that appear in some papers, where one clue may give two or more equally valid solutions and where the decision on the winner is at the editor's discretion. These are really a form of gambling. I have nothing against gambling, but it doesn't seem to me to have any place in crosswords proper. Where it does appear it can only debase crosswords as an art form, which may sound high-falutin (gorgeous word!) but isn't really. For a well-designed crossword can give genuine aesthetic pleasure, not only to the compiler, but to the solver as well; it brings a 'bitter-sweet mixture of bewilderment and delight' in Ivor Brown's words; and above all it is *right*, it jells—a good crossword is as beautiful as a sonnet. And like a sonnet it uses a strict form and fairly rigid canons. But I really am beginning to sound high-falutin now!

The people who assemble crosswords are all sorts and conditions of men and women—parsons, retired bank managers, lecturers, schoolmasters, engineers, housewives. They are not cranks with twisted minds, but however they work and however long it takes them to compile a puzzle (one *Guardian* man does the whole thing in his head, grid and all, before putting pen to paper) they all have one thing in common—a love of words and of the curious links that can be made with them. For this, English is ideal, for it is a joyously comic language. In what other tongue would one find in quick succession such oddities as:

Gallipot (a small glazed pot)
Gallise (in wine-making, to bring to standard proportions by adding sugar and water to inferior must)
Gallium (a rare metallic element)
Gallivant (to gad about)
Galliswasp (a West Indian lizard)
Galloglass (an ancient Irish armed retainer)
Gallopade (a quick kind of dance)
Gallows-bird (one who deserves hanging)
Galloway (a type of horse)
Gally (to scare)
Galoot (a soldier)
Galosh, galore, galumph, and so on?

Of course, many of these are uncommon words, the sort you only come across normally when you are deep in a dictionary. And while crossword compilers may have to resort to the dictionary from time to time to find the right word for a particularly sticky corner, the less they have to do so the better, at any rate as far as puzzles published in daily newspapers are concerned. It is unfair to expect the great body of readers (many of them doing the crossword on their way to work by train or bus in the morning) to have Chambers Twentieth Century Dictionary in their briefcase. It is a very good dictionary and the authority for *Guardian* puzzles as well as many others. But it is 1,400 pages long, three inches wide, and weighs three and a half pounds—not the sort of thing one can slip in a jacket-pocket. The best puzzles, in any case, are often those compiled without the aid of a dictionary, those in which witty clueing leads to words or phrases that are part of the accepted language, written or spoken. This doesn't mean that all puzzles are, or should be, at the same level of difficulty. The crossword editor of a daily paper tends to find that his mail consists in almost equal parts of complaints that (a) the puzzles are too difficult and (b) they are too easy. Sometimes too there is a gratifying letter of praise. When Paul Jennings protested in the *Guardian* that the clueing of one puzzle was not merely obscure but double obscure, that the light was 'no light but rather darkness visible', another reader rang up to say that the puzzles had become far too simple; once they had taken her all day to solve—now they only took until midday. And what, poor soul, was she to do with her afternoons? I'm not sure what this proves, except that there is no such animal as the average crossword solver. Some do it on the 7.40 to town, some on the flight to Lisbon, some between washing up the breakfast things and starting on the baby's nappies, some as a relief from the monotony of a hospital bed, some on the promenade at Blackpool, some when rain stops play. We have never tried on the *Guardian* to please all the people all the time—you end up with stereotyped stuff that is dull to everyone. We have preferred to publish puzzles of varying degrees of difficulty to suit varying standards of skill. Some days the addict will finish a puzzle in ten minutes; at other times it may take him three-quarters of an hour. The only thing we insist on is that, easy or difficult, they should be good of their kind. And in this book there is something to suit everybody.

Now, a plain man's guide to clueing. The first crossword puzzle published by *The Manchester Guardian* appeared in the late 1920s at a time when clues were only just developing from the stage of straight definitions. You still get definition clues these days—but not in the *Guardian*, if we can help it. They have survived almost intact in American puzzles, however, which became fossilised about 1925 and are virtually unreadable. Definitions are dull—but how about double meanings? 'Undiluted bull,' for instance. That's NEAT. In other words, undiluted equals neat, as in whisky, and bull equals neat as in the old word for cattle. Of course, you can have more than two meanings if you like. 'Deputy in the grip of depravity'. That's VICE. Often you will get anagrams—too often, some people think, though some of the best clues ever created are in this form. Anagrams ought, somehow or other, to indicate that they are anagrams. 'Imputes false motive' is a pithy clue for IMPETUS, with 'imputes' the anagram, 'false' indicating that rearrangement is necessary, and 'motive' giving an idea of the meaning. Another one—'What the viewer sees in TV is a puzzle' for VISTA, which is what the viewer sees, 'TV is a' as the anagram, and 'puzzle' indicating rearrangement. Another one, a traditional dig 'Cost—this upsets these people' for SCOTTISH. What about 'Women of strange views' for WIVES?

There is also 'Les Miserables—or The Turn of the Screw' for WRETCHES, and 'One's last excursion, but it could be real fun' for FUNERAL. Some anagrams can be decidedly tricky. 'Pass the rum please' is pretty misleading for ELAPSE, and what about 'He doesn't believe in field-marshals' for INFIDEL, where 'marshals' indicates the rearrangement of 'in field', or 'He's performing in the circle' for SPHERE, or 'Sweet miscreant' for NECTAR?

Anagrams may be combined with other forms of clueing, of course, especially initials. 'Rich upper class lady affected by liquor' gives HYDRAULIC, a combination of 'rich lady' with U. Initials may also occur in other words that are broken up into their components for the purpose of clueing, e.g. 'Horseback tour beginning for reformer' for COB/BET/T and 'Opening Daily Express may make dejected if not cross' which, with the X removed ('if not cross') gives D/EPRESS. 'Building erected to a deity in Pennsylvania' produces P/A/GOD/A, in which P at the beginning and A at the end are accepted abbreviations for the American state. Other abbreviations met with are:

A.B.   for sailor
AC   account, bill
AD   modern times, or advertisement
AG   silver
ALA   Alabama (and similarly for other states)
ANS   answer
ARR   arrives, arranged
ARA   painter
ARP   Air raid precautions (now obsolescent)
ASS   Association
BA (and BD, BSC, MA, etc.)   graduates
BC   before Christ
C   chapter, cent, one hundred, about (circa)
CE   Church of England, Establishment

xii

CH   Companion of Honour, chief, church
CID   detectives
CO   commanding officer, company
CON   against
D   penny, five hundred
DD   Doctor of Divinity
DO   the same (ditto)
DR   doctor, debtor
E   English, East (compare N, S, W—cardinal points)
ED   editor
EE   errors excepted
EG   for example
ENG   England, English
ER   the Queen
F   forte, i.e. strongly
FD   Defender of the Faith
FE   iron
FEM   feminine
FT   foot, feet
G   gram, gravity
GB   Great Britain
GEN   general
GI   soldier
GP   doctor
HO   house
HR   hour
IC   in charge
ID   the same
IE   that is
IN   inches
INST   this month
L   lake, pound, fifty, learner
LB   pound
M   monsieur, thousand
MA   graduate
MD   Doctor of Medicine
MM   millimetre
MO and MOH   medical officer
MP   Member of Parliament
MPH   miles per hour

MR and MRS
MS and MSS   manuscripts
MT   mount
N   north
NAT   born
NE   North-east (similarly NW, SW, SE)
NO   number
NT   New Testament
O   zero, love, duck (scores)
OB   died
OC   Officer Commanding
OM   Order of Merit
OT   Old Testament
OP   work
P   piano, i.e. softly
PC   constable, Privy Counsellor
PER   by
PM   afternoon, Prime Minister
PO   post office
PR   public relations
PRO   professional, for
PS
PT   physical training
QC   Queen's counsel
R   king, queen, take (recipe)
RA   Royal Academy or Academician, i.e. painter, Royal
      Artillery, i.e. gunners
RC   Roman Catholic, Red Cross
RE   concerning, about, Royal Engineers, i.e. sappers
RD   road
RH   right hand
RIP   requiescat in pace
RLY and RY   railway
RM   Royal Marines
RN   Royal Navy
RU   Rugby Union
RV   Revised Version
S   South
SA   South Africa
SC   to wit

SEC   secretary
SEN   senator, senior
SS   steamship, liner
ST   saint, street
TA   Territorial Army (now obsolescent)
TT   teetotaller, races
TV   television
U   universal
UK   United Kingdom
ULT   last
V   five, against
VC   Victoria Cross
W   West
WD   War Department
X   unknown (in algebra), ten

Not all these crop up equally frequently, and, of course, other initials and prefixes may be used as well. Many puzzles will not have them at all. But they are useful to bear in mind.

Some of the prefixes are Latin—'per', 'pro', and so on. Other foreign words occur, but where they do they are generally of the simplest. Most people will recognise LE, LA, or LES in 'The French' and DER in 'German article'. An unusual one, however, is 'Foreign John and Mary about to go to pot' for MARI/JUAN/A—straightforward translations of foreign names.

Palindromes (words or phrases that read the same backwards as forward) are another form of clueing. The most famous example is probably to be found in Adam's first words to Eve—'Madam, I'm Adam'. Others—'French statesman gives himself up' for LAVAL, 'Even gets the same rise' for LEVEL, and 'Act either way' for DEED. There are also reversals—'Getting up a riotous party in the bar' for REVEL, which is LEVER back to front. LAMINA gives ANIMAL. Reversals can be made up of two or more words, e.g. 'Call me backward? That's sickening!' for EM/ETIC, and only part reversals, e.g. 'The outcast finds father hair-raising' for PA/RIAH. Solutions can sometimes be found hidden in the clue—'Some ball I'd slash through the covers' for LIDS. There are also 'sound' clues, such as 'Animal naked, we hear' for BEAR. One type of puzzle found more often in the *Guardian* than in other papers consists for the most part of variations on a theme. These puzzles are not so difficult as they may appear at first sight, though it can be a bit disconcerting to light on '1 across—See 25 down'. In fact, the theme running through the puzzle is likely to be a reasonably familiar one with a pretty simple key. Once the key is found the puzzle falls into place, perhaps almost too quickly

This is not an exhaustive guide—almost infinite combinations of clueing are possible—but it includes the chief forms to be met with. Every compiler has a different way of thinking and about a dozen compilers are represented here. The knack of solving the puzzles depends on getting behind the mind of the compiler, which, as you will see, is not as hard as it sounds Finally, four favourite clues:

'Men's my one failing'—Mother of Nine (MNEMOSYNE)

'I engage idolaters to produce leading articles'

(EDITORIALS)

'Is it Parliament or the Church that makes men twisters?'

(WESTMINSTER)

and 'Wilson taken to court for going back on his word'

(WOO/DROW)

PUZZLES

(Solutions at back of book)

1

ACROSS

1. Dual nationality, it appears on the surface (6, 6).
8. Letter composition of minor company (7).
9. Was cleaning lady about, anyway, to provide this? (3, 4).
11. Back—no, it's round at the depot (7).
12. Most splendid church begins to be encompassed by strange rites (7).
13. He gets up the step (5).
14. Ball race broken, nothing to add; gentleman can go by horse (9).
16. A Curia rule pointlessly made up concerning confessions (9).
19. Wallet for share certificates (5).
21. Having striven, disordered, turns over (7).
23. Comfortable, half full in artist's stand (7).
24. Send into quarters for solitary (7).
25. Supervise poetry in Old English (7).
26. Stars of usual conversion, converted to one of these like stars appearing (4, 2, 6).

DOWN

1. Instinct fights about when to fast (7).
2. Sooner peer—that is right (7).
3. Oil-can can be made according to rule (9).
4. This horse is champion in practice start (5).
5. Cyril alters restlessly, turns poetic (7).
6. Scene in which the French rise up with unequal sides (7).
7. Actions, verve—that would be a change for the party! (12).
10. Preacher, go and cast spell in other assembly! (3, 9).
15. 14 takes a pole in place of fifty to build his home town, possibly (9).
17. I arrive dishevelled at the coast (7).
18. Hearty company right face (7).
19. Of charity, possibly, resists change (7).
20. Umpire employs and declines (7).
22. Bundle he goes in safely halfway (5).

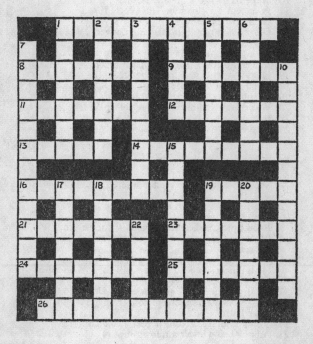

2

ACROSS

8. Sir Walter's charm? (8).
9. Walton wrote his life—fellow-angler? (6).
10. Make us do it for the artist? (6).
11. Impudent way to enter Tim's form (8).
12. Game performance? (4).
13. Garret Sikh rebuilt is the main danger, perhaps (5-5).
15. Country gathering in spring? (7).
16. Run in McRae's piano composition (7).
18. Plant in these areas for a change (6-4).
19. Some of the language—! (4).
20. Intent on seeing us after 10 (8).
22. Was in van and also outside it in Spain (6).
23. Inventor No. 11 retires? (6).
24. Tom is one to show feelings, possibly (8).

DOWN

1. Shows bowler-hat to me I'd ordered around August 24 (11-4).
2. Did these fliers overlook a tempting locality? (5, 2, 8).
3. Breaks promise about cask and is troublesome (10).
4. Where we might drink the odd gins and get some cricket (7).
5. Pretend to have some cash, among other things (4).
6. High officer has Rodin pieces, all sorts, round the room (4, 11).
7. Plant produces nine-pound seeds—clear? (6, 9).
14. Perhaps some amusement concerning Haydn's work (10).
17. Sailor embraces eccentric pest in the bar (7).
21. Admits being in certain townships (4).

3

ACROSS

1. Something done by pupils gets the cane, possibly (11).
8. Perhaps early part of recess (4).
10. Object to strike in one of the services? (6-4).
11. 1 game? (4).
14. Tend to take union's direction (5).
15. Fail again, being careless (6).
17. Hinders printing of foreign poems (6).
19. Does Thomson gain a lot out of music? (9-6).
20. Out with string ensemble, recording (6).
22. The cricketer on the hearth? (6).
23. A sound curtain appears to answer the purpose (5).
24. Fly back with pungency (4).
27. Hiawatha's driver for practising one's swing? (6, 4).
28. River smell, say? (4).
29. Shows formality to a certain degree, about retiring from court (4, 7).

DOWN

2. The artist of Gettysburg (4).
3. Gives amusement to a large number, making money (4).
4. Rules for guides going round Gateshead (6).
5. Charitable revel organised by old comedian (6, 9).
6. Visited valley with airman climber (6).
7. One lobster was distributed among the servants (5, 6).
9. Support chief officer and arrange advertising, perhaps? (10).
12. Forewarning before space traveller carries it in ascent (11).
13. Meaning a direction to church of some consequence? (10).
16. Exhibition of oils alone (5).
18. Wear certain lines after some hesitation (5).
21. Mount horse to catch bird (6).
22. Flier, about fifty, appears to shrink back (6).
25. Fruit in the best position? (4).
26. Skilful, as Adamson said (4).

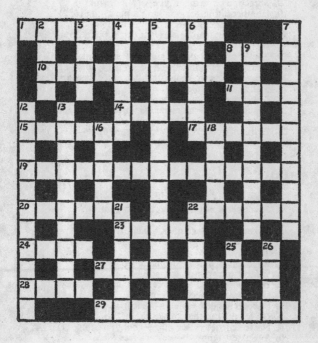

4

ACROSS

4. On the ship, roughly aft, and easily broken (8).
8. Manage to hear the composer (6).
9. Someone on farm, a type seen in Spain (8).
10. Compensating for breaking a pink mug (6, 2).
11. Note traveller's opening commission (6).
12. Perhaps he heard of broken ties in the old railway (8).
13. Shows offhandedness, giving 6s. in change (8).
16. Attractive person carrying note is to call back (8).
19. Leave letters to Redhead in the office, perhaps (8).
21. Vulgar tract? (6).
23. Concerning principal general (8).
24. What the office manager might do to help the traveller? (8).
25. Drink plan backed by Richardson (6).
26. Poet finds fish satisfactory (8).

DOWN

1. Like rearing a girl in a Biblical district (7).
2. A copper upset detectives, getting into trouble—it's a habit! (9).
3. Take port in December, generally? (6).
4. Provides lodgings with telephone, etc.—a Mr Turner (10, 5).
5. Rage about damaged bins in London (8).
6. Collect the sound beams (5).
7. Well, you haven't got this! (7).
14. Out to avoid meeting people? (3, 2, 4).
15. Bob exchanged phaeton for carriage (8).
17. Do away with the bails? Oh, that's wrong! (7).
18. Native carrier raised club—could be drunk (7).
20. In Sussex, empty houses are free (6).
22. Crazy to carry on with unit (5).

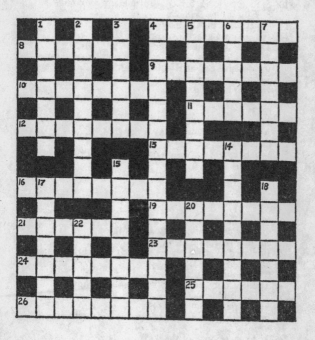

5

ACROSS

1. Famous son of famous father on the 9 (5, 6).
8. I leave Russia's first operatic prince (4).
10. Setting to work briskly—fortunately avoiding putting on the 9 (8, 2).
11. Superlative post in the orchard (4).
14. Fly in amid general rejoicing (5).
15, 17. King's renounced one on the 9 (6, 6).
19. A consideration before actually putting on the 9— the decisive one at Highland Games (6, 2, 3, 4).
20. Vehicles not reversed with American petrol (6).
22. He who hesitates . . . (6).
23. . . . Is comprehensively lost in doctrinal liturgies (2, 3).
24. Three making trouble (4).
27. A hundred 4? Yes, in any order (2, 4, 4).
28. Cats become does (4).
29. What general confusion he caused British 22 downs on many a 9 (6, 5).

DOWN

2. Notice in angles Pythagoras used (4).
3. Quietly withdrawn petty artist (4).
4. In for a reception (2, 4).
5. Prepared to strike on the 9—facing the firing squad? (5, 2, 3, 1, 4).
6. Cut on the 9 (6).
7. The lizard in the quarry is giving warning (11).
9. Links go for clues (4, 6).
12. Ealing tiara made level (11).
13. Impoverished county, one to dun for resettlement (4-3-3).
16. The sphere once of the 9 (5).
18. Legal body a mule is easier to shift (5).
21. A quarter that is staked at first in nap (6).
22. Skilled performer on the 9, by name and nature (6).
25. A small point in the 24, 28 (4).
26. Only a 9 (4).

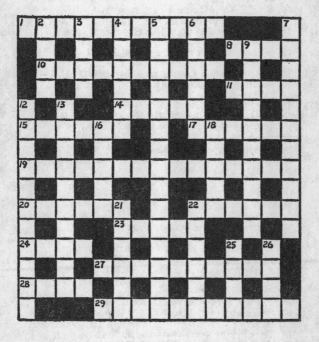

6

ACROSS

1. Place of perfume, with rating in song (6).
5. An extreme republican, said Mr Maudling regretfully (8).
9, 10, 23. The M1 near a back street in entertainments from 1 ... (8, 3, 3, 6).
11. ... recounted by poor little Ezra: hard cheese! (12).
13. Magistrate from 1—and no gentleman, I may add! (4).
14. Get-together in reverse yet separately (3-5).
17. Sporting affair briefly involved handkerchief and magazine (8).
18. See 22.
20. Time out for Louis XVIII, less and lighter than 9, 10, 23 (1, 7, 4).
23. See 9.
24. Way to escape a roundabout journey to earth?
25. Promulgation of a case in the United States (8).
26. Untidy effect of 8 (6).

DOWN

2. German city goes back on short time (4).
3. German city where the candle burns crooked? (9).
4. Inability to care less, in a way, next year (6).
5. Flag in a wind, treble-hued (3, 5, 3, 4).
6. A relative inside stimulus to reach 1, 2, 3, or 7 (2, 6).
7. 13 on end (5).
8. The baring of French, in and out for a change (10).
12. Safe seats? (4-6).
15. See 19.
16. Tweed being worn by Ainsworth? (8).
19, 15. Good man from the 9, 10, 23; ah! Claud 16? (6, 9).
21. May he run for prime minister? (5).
22, 18. Accommodation with an upper limit? (4, 4).

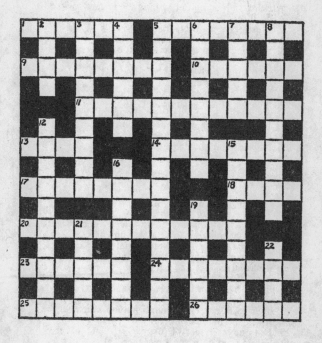

7

ACROSS

1. Now available: opus 100, for the pipe (4-4).
5. Slave girl with Bible backing (6).
9. Below, a mouse after visiting the farmer's wife of ill repute (8).
10. Blush for a plausible loan? (6).
12. Letter for a Yorkshire river? (5).
13. Bad king about to eat at a point that's very sharp (5-4).
14. Unplanned arrival: debts follow it (12).
18. Object of a scramble? (8, 4).
21. Muse I need when hurt by Furies (9).
23. Number of a French novel (5).
24. After 6 the painter's not at all well (6).
25. 10, nothing fast, for smelling (8).
26. Despatched a second time? (6).
27. Flower in an old shape (8).

DOWN

1. Not much of an insult (6).
2. The beast has to wade across . . . (6).
3. . . . The revolutionary boss evidently doesn't! (9).
4. Louts laughingly call at a toss-up (7-5).
6. Left one's bed—name immaterial (5).
7. Flower or sweetmeat containing cocaine? (8).
8. Bestowal of legs and ears? (8).
11. Lack of inclination—to do anything? (12).
15. Bright burner with likely victim? (5-4).
16. Scientific character of the verb "rose"? (8).
17. Spur to discovery of tumili among saints (8).
19. Await the devil at last (6).
20. Not out yet? Nearly! (6).
22. Fabric used by many Londoners (5).

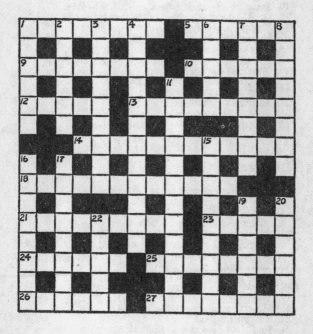

8

ACROSS

8. Someone going to say it? (8).
9. You start soon—when May comes (6).
10. Some people always have an excuse! (4).
11, 12. P.C. Hunt interested in musical pieces? (3, 7, 6).
14. Perhaps racks appear wrong—sure to need altering (8).
15. Brook shows courage? (7).
17. Appears flashy, from the service angle (7).
20. Miss turning? (8).
22. Failure on one river or another (6).
23. Sport of loud Altcar types in Gateshead (4-6).
24. Barbarian became his leader (4).
25. Stroke made by novice? Nonsense! (6).
26. Plentiful materials for sailor and foreign worker (8).

DOWN

1. Sailors hold everything up in Australia (8).
2. Girl writing against time (4).
3. Captain of a steamer? (6).
4. Man has a follower in Canada (7).
5. Say their parts with wild emotion (8).
6. Slapped as a prisoner might be? (10).
7. Leg can look broken (6).
13. Call about four, in this case (10).
16. Showing disapproval of people in the mews? (3-5).
18. Mocking youthful interest? (8).
19. Said to include part of a path (7).
21. Mean to stand drink to a score (6).
22. Boat shelter? (6).
24. Soldier of French type joins similar writer (4).

9

ACROSS

1. Bank where you'll find 12, where 8, 3 and 24 have a vested interest safeguarding 5 down (3, 3).
5. Rose shrivelled in time: how annoying (8).
9. Nail box having enough strength (8).
10. Attack cost (6).
11. I sit up with some pair bent on a covenant affirmation (2, 2, 1, 7).
13. Gossip with a cat from overseas (4).
14. Land superior volume order (8).
17. Remove and execute (5, 3).
18. Thanks to Lawrence a gallery is provided (4).
20. Resent atomic variety of scientific instruments (12).
23. Sally distorted case given half of 2 (6).
24. Recommend an expert on 5 down (8).
25. Lose, did I? Adored the exchanges, anyway (8).
26. One informed on 5 down securing no try without a conversion (6).

DOWN

2. Novelist with confidence (4).
3. 1 outside the street spots another expert on 5 down (9).
4. Confound the animal (6).
5. What halted felon? (anag.) (See 1, 24, 26, 3, 6, 8, 12 and 16) (3, 3, 2, 3, 4).
6. Instrument of 5 down (8).
7. Fit maps turning up without direction (5).
8. Aga comes to terms with it—yet another expert on 5 down (10).
12. He'd cut case possibly, one on a 10 by 5 down (3, 7).
15. The most recent fashion—long delayed at the wicket? (6, 3).
16. Sore corn contorts experts on 5 down (8).
19. Holidays at Norwegian capital permeate with an influence (6).
21. Completely indisposed with an ill-directed insertion (2, 3).
22. Turn round where 12 may end up (4).

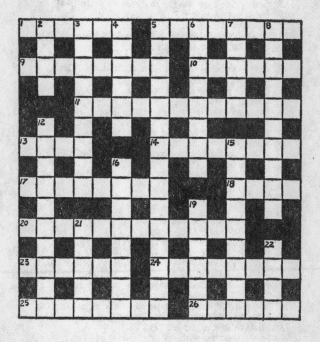

10

ACROSS

7. Fit maps turning up without direction (5). (7).
8. Beast with eggs having to cheer vulgarly (3-4).
10. Beast gets a return half on part of the French railways (6).
11. Beast detects duke with honourable learner (3-5).
12. Beast to make an attack upon? (4).
13. Beast or brickbat? (4-6).
14. Beast at the piano with the right song? That's the song-writer (7-4).
19. Beast wants to grieve nearly a week before the Ides of March (4-6).
22. Beast of malevolent character (4).
23. Beast—a sort of nag in the tableland (8).
24. Beast with the backing of two males (6).
25. Beast with a little place en masse (7).
26. Beast, unsteady type, creates an awkward situation for the queen (7).

DOWN

1. Grow after exposure (7).
2. Surgeon said 'hallo' to (8).
3. It sounds a major item in the kitchen (6).
4. Birds of dawning (4-4).
5. Take, read, and digest 'The Sailors' World' (6).
6. Norse contribution to Etruscan diction (7).
9. Prison edict wanted for wanted man, perhaps (11).
15. One certain to be converted very quickly (2, 1, 5).
16. Early Bird: make a statement—about security (8).
17. How to raise up classical port (7).
18. Mistake in the garden (7).
20. Swallow spirit without breaking a gun (6).
21. I am a means of travelling north for a sign of sanctity (6).

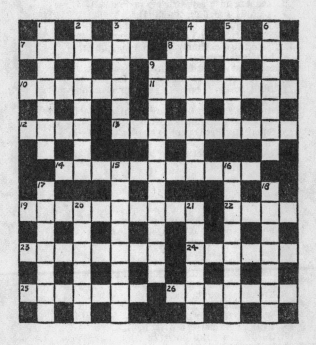

11

ACROSS

1. State cut back is in USA (12).
8. Worker we rap heartlessly in Belgium (7).
9. Redhead in noisy quarters in France (7).
11. A growl I made in India (7).
12. 'Aida' put into production in Pakistan (7).
13. Sharp stroke in Las Palmas, seemingly (5).
14. Note tribal assembly before a king on the Mediterranean (9).
16. Soar and sag as if by turns in Spain (9).
19. Some slut one encountered in England (5).
21. 10 Stand by in point-to-point stretches anywhere (7).
23. Right in English (and in French) in USA (7).
24. Moaners discomfited in Italy (3, 4).
35. Stood for Parliament—you don't say!—in Burma (7).
26. New moon belief not to lose heart in South Africa (12).

DOWN

1. Sad, yet having had a ripping time (2, 5).
2. English river-bank? No, it's in Aberdeenshire (7).
3. Wriggler and vigilant watcher around a vegetable (9).
4. Total with a drawback (3-2).
5. Pole engaged in Utopia's exploitation of cactus (7).
6. Unresolved but bound to develop in it (2, 5).
7. Crafty skippers grab steamers at random (5-7).
10. Suitable 'Music while you work' for chef (8, 4).
15. Type Fe is right as a trivet (5-4).
17. Oil transferred to liner (7).
18. Italians—silly people with no income? (7).
19. One of those fabrics without number having undeveloped power (7).
20. To ring without delay is premature (3, 4).
22. Bogus card game (5).

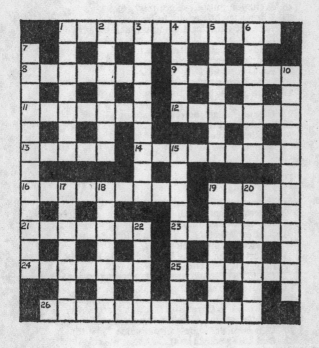

12

ACROSS

1. Put down to drink having decreased, as it were? (10).
6. Well, you must have got this! (6).
9. Chronicler brings girl to heel (8).
10. Poor view in a cart going through the grounds? (8).
11. Many animals are females (6).
12. The way rent collector is exposed (8).
14. Amazes us at dons' gathering (8).
16. Blockhead gets free drink in Dorset (8).
19. Nice gaps adapted for slipping out (8).
21. Coming publicity opening (6).
22. Creature might be seen in spring (8).
23. Lamb appears in a vessel that is golden (8).
24. His love accomplished nothing (6).
25. Writer of twelve letters about Mrs Thrale (10).

DOWN

1. Expose wreck who comes in to drink (4, 2).
2. Entertainment got up in many Alpine villages (4).
3. Girl sent to mend locks (8).
4. Part of Wiltshire sisal production goes to Lancashire town—clear? (9, 5).
5. A sort of sea change in London (4, 3),
7. Birds raised in Ulster, generally (6).
8. Cupid not employed in this plant? (4-2-8).
13. Tend to err about a poet (5).
15. Sorry to have to study hackneyed composition (8).
17. Left book in Cornwall (7).
18. Articles about long disturbance in Africa (6).
20. Village of Palestine—an old name for it (6).
22. Bird gets steamed? (4).

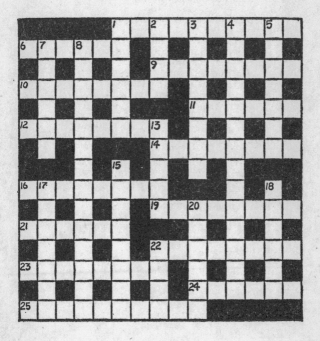

13

ACROSS

1, 5. Forced to leave the room, being deprived
   (3, 2, 2, 7).
10, 11. Remain sanguine—not in St Paul's view?
   (4, 3, 3, 4).
12, 13. Bert's dire error—breeding dogs (6, 8).
14. County 13 (9).
16. Pound balanced in 14 or Fife (5).
17, 19. Flash making the hinges glint (5, 9).
23. One way—moon-faced . . . (8).
24. . . . and another—entertaining (6).
26, 27. The present record? (10, 4).
28. Bird broken hearted—get her? . . . (7).
29. . . . is she French? (7).

DOWN

2. Lover turns up in Lagos or Omaha (7).
3. 12 river . . . (5).
4. . . . try river leave (2, 5).
6. Stick? Where? (6).
7. Had beer in for islander (9).
8. Soup surgeon soon left rising (7).
9. Passing by, retiring to tempt possibly (13).
15. Try to get up about noon and bow in order to
    genuflect (5, 4).
18. Willing recipient? (7).
20. Cakes he made for chipmunks (7).
21. Indifferent gear? (7).
22. Critical pointer (6).
25. Dog charges among the bric-a-brac, head first (5).

14

ACROSS

1. Any premarital arrangement involving the House (13).
10. All, for example, or ninety-nine; emblematic (9)
11. Partial reduction, about a penny, returned to milk producer (5).
12. Entangle a composer (5).
13. Volume of impressions (5, 4).
14. 12 in back street trips (7).
16. Example of speechifying to the point (7).
18. Apparatus for making alcoholic beverage with doctor in charge (7).
20. State of 1,000 other ranks, an officer, another officer (7).
21. He let in two points at the end of October (9).
23. Tear about softly, there's a division (5).
24. Chose to demolish depot (5).
25. In nature's gloomy order (9).
26. Snake-eating office charmer? (9, 4).

DOWN

2. Relieve patriarch in a tardy situation (9).
3. In-law, age up in the fifties (5).
4. Sartre's composition catches attention (7).
5. Embrace and start necking in strange places (7).
6. Player starts tune with spirit: namely Rock (9).
7. Instrument turned back to avoid a row (5).
8. Equality? Rubbish—style is purely mechanical! (6, 7).
9. Set bolt as a consequence? (6, 7).
15. Bride more likely to make her dress (9).
17. Strange device of creole six (9).
19. Oil vessel bearing strange secrets (7).
20. Lizard found in school (7).
22. For turning the French to the English (5).
23. Brush up religion in vehicle (5).

15

ACROSS

1. 'How often will it bounce?' suggests improvidence (5, 3, 6).
8. The name in Europe for victory is poison (5).
9. Defunct flatfish comes in to be cooked (8).
11. Sluggard writes German song about American president (3-4)
12. Don't give the sailor a mark (7).
13. The English point of view? (5).
15. There could be nothing risky with her pudding (9).
17. Let the boiler out? (5, 4).
20. Plain but far from flat (5).
21. Coloured boat? Produce another version (7).
23. Crumbly but ready for cooking (7).
25. Guide's mother swallowed by monster (8).
26. National flag with aspiration (5).
27. Fast train on the wrong line's so poker-faced (14).

DOWN

1. It's possible that Satan is concerned—how audacious! (5-3-4).
2. Boat or vessel (Old English) (5).
3. Embers I've made a note of (9).
4. Approximately every other 12 (7).
5. The pessimism of the French couple (7).
6. Where Charles lost his head? (5).
7. More turning of the tide to deport (9).
10. The king's been upset about echoes—there's nothing less for legwear (4-8).
14. Not an upright piano for a farceur of the French race (5, 4).
16. What should be below Calphurnia? (9).
18. The neck is like this, without number (7).
19. Taking a piece of beef, may be fined by a Turk (7).
22. Sounds prophetic but is a bore (5).
24. Maybe I get a bit of shade (5).

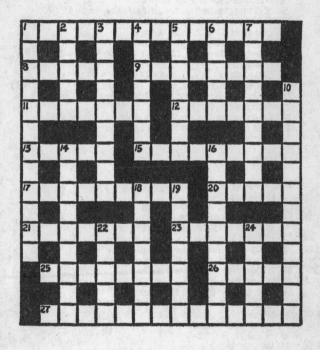

16

ACROSS

1. Former regent put together for huge effect (6, 3, 6).
8. Welsh abuse on board? (8).
9. Microphone under the pillow? The vermin! (6).
10. Christened Andrew over the water? (8).
11. The struggle of Sisyphus (16).
13. Pity one gets onto the range (10).
16. Draw out round a street: the year starts with spring (10).
19. Encirclement is fair game (4-2).
20. H means trouble (3, 5).
21. Universal sort of saint for East-West churchmen (6).
22. A student in the smoke—one with a cabinet (8).
23. Wilmot the poet at cooler, fresher fruit (4, 2, 9).

DOWN

1, 2. Become so thick as to need putting out? (3, 2, 4, 1, 5, 2, 4).
3. European article on seed (6).
4. European concept may be rich to Fred (5, 5).
5. Inverted feast, related to a fly-under? (8).
6. Hebrew receptacle in Arabic with no lid (8).
7. Spare time member of the Black Watch? (8, 7).
12. Like a scarecrow, hardly pro tapioca (10).
14. Waldensian maybe is bare to—his shoes? (8).
15. It's up for hire to a killer (8).
17. One law he broke temporarily (6).
18. Difficulty of a Southern characteristic (6).

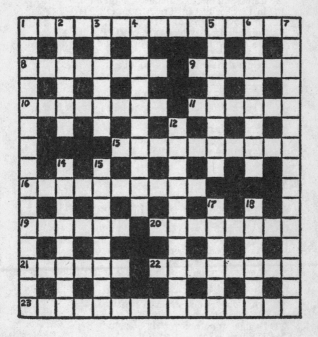

17

ACROSS

1. Premier sees how to cap Borsch with Irish stew (14).
9. Caresses non-U abandoned children (9).
10. In Durban turbans are African (5).
11. The obvious way to go? (5).
12. So Leghorn may be on the coast (9).
13. Do something original—where good cheer is egg-shaped (8).
14. Peninsular scene of his trial (6).
17. Drink approximately about a cent (6).
19. Scott's mascot (8).
22. Change the weight of a bird (9).
24. 'They haven't got no ——, the fallen sons of Eve' (Chesterton) (5).
25. Bella's other name (5).
26. Is it used to divide the national income? (4, 5).
27. Stay in the air for always and always (5-5, 4).

DOWN

1. Face it—only fate is involved with love (14).
2. Where one isn't even able to eat? (7).
3. A vile garb displayed in London (9).
4. Tiny lies reveal a degenerate age, as it were (8).
5. 'Play on,' he said, or do wrong to love (6).
6. A pun about transport (5).
7. Honesty, and nothing besides, in a low fellow (7).
8. The Hanoverians reign, as everyone knows (5, 5, 4).
15. Sail that needs fastening in the Snake River (9).
16. What does 'Volk' mean in Russian? (8).
18. The wire round the city isn't fatal (7).
20. Having trouble, inversely—or straits (7).
21. The bird takes a count (6).
23. What do you do about five fish? (5).

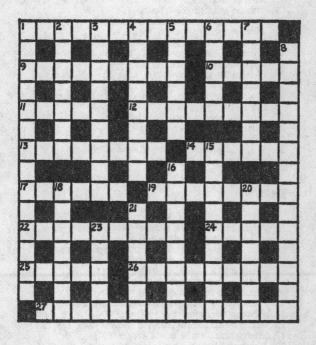

18

ACROSS

1. The P.M. rises, wreathed in smiles (7).
5. Retired clergyman takes a drink—causes talk (7).
9. Vehicle used in the islands? (5).
10. Perhaps lukewarm drinks for dogs (9).
11. Money Incas collected for monk (10).
12. Formerly part of Roncesvalles (4).
14. Protectors aren't commonly like Andrew (6, 5).
18. Approve appearance? (11).
21. Like to be given an extra note, the poisonous creatures! (4).
22. Churchman is in favour of state altering part of Bible (10).
25. Bird has some sort of crest (9).
26. Girl with a heart of stone? (5).
27. Ailment dies out with change by sea (7).
28. Minority protest in Norfolk town—roughly ten (7).

DOWN

1. Start to show to advantage? (3, 3).
2. Might include Don Turner—one of seven (6).
3. Mince pie team can get free (10).
4. Lines from original Conrad work, perhaps? (5).
5. Left a county in N. Ireland (9).
6. Many a poem written in this vein (4).
7. Evil can ruin a Spanish city (8).
8. Particulars of relations? (8).
13. Like people including one in calumnies (10).
15. Fashion part of a ship in Kent (9).
16. Being discarded, exchanged blows, some say (8).
17. Strengthens drinks containing wine (8).
19. Is interrupting farewell, in this case (6).
20. Affirm the whereabouts of cricket enthusiasts? (6).
23. It makes clothes—for angling in? (5).
24. A time to stand one's ground, perhaps (4).

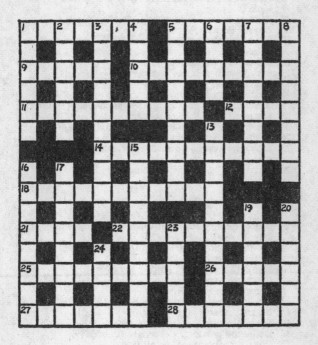

19

ACROSS

7. Is Penny sorry to return flag? (5).
8. Fasten back after breaking off end of corner stone (9).
9. Premier indicates appropriate setting for the Royal Society (5).
10. Have unsettled debt with the railways—outstanding conduct? (9).
12. Bill can be responsible (11).
16. Risk it with a bit of satire (4).
17. Hearing test? (5).
18. Dash—that's the spirit (4).
19. Absolute cat! For example a great many, more advanced than I, have spoken out (11).
22. Point to follow: truncate prepared speech (9).
24. Fruit for a Scot from the French (5).
25. Elaborate procedure makes a mockery of my trial (9).
26. Inclined to let article be included (5).

DOWN

1. Dog comes up around it when cook is out—for tea? (5, 4).
2. Who must be prepared in this organisation (3, 6).
3. At the centre, or in church (4).
4. Not collected; quite unnecessary (8-3).
5. Clear open country (5).
6. Worth the price? (5).
11. Qualified, but at the start is without direction; it's unavoidable (11).
13. Discriminating, by the accent (5).
14. Delightful creature, measure the outside (9).
15. Equal to a horse, above all (9).
20. Steals up to the seat (5).
21. Say, me cloak's shabby (5).
23. East Central (4).

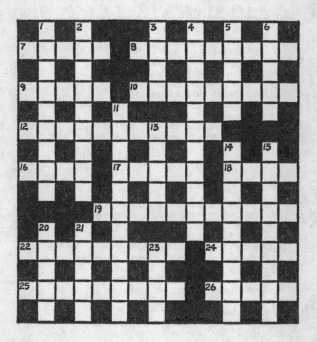

20

ACROSS

8. Turn half left, then right in the ditch—that's weird . . . (8).
9. . . . turn over in vehicle and he may catch one! (6).
10. Surprise is not planned for ship's officer (6).
11. Lack of spirit perhaps makes boys tire badly (8).
12. Forward at the proper time (4).
13. Split heads can be tender! (4-6).
15. Make endeavour at allure (7).
16. Bang out madly at armed vessel (3-4).
18. Income from earthquake? (6, 4).
19. Language in absurd usage (4).
20. Silver shred loses colour, distorts and withers (8).
22. Idea of gold they are about (6).
23. Protection in case we harm ourselves (6).
24. Initial dividend before brewery conversion bears fruit (8).

DOWN

1. Leicester roughs carve up the county (15).
2. Destroy schooner—scrub it—burn one's boats (5, 3, 7).
3. Like heavenly figure in Hollywood? (4-6).
4. Weed let go badly after this (7).
5. Backs end of lock-out, turns black-leg (4).
6. Hardy characteristic of Elfride (1, 4, 2, 4, 4).
7. Tighten nuts to fix those subject to play? (6, 9).
14. Consider by number, yet heartlessly admit one lies within (6, 4).
17. Resort for treatment of disease (7).
21. Describes circuit and lands right in the eye (4).

21

ACROSS

1. Likely result—room to turn (6, 4).
8. Copy for the choir (4).
10. Hanging garlands for another go of tennis (10).
11. Pirate after 23 or before 26 (4).
13. Probably Cornish not French bonds (7).
15. Over-bold but maybe polished (6).
16. Novel source of love? (6).
17. Our revenge on 1, thanks to 26s and 22s (2, 3, 3, 3, 4).
18. Girl in checks, perhaps (6).
20. Calm cool head in a Highlander (6).
21. Number submitted for a competition for a one-way street (2, 5).
22. Avoid an endearment (4).
25. Delightful spelling! (10).
26. Extract information about 22's diet (4).
27. Little Lesley, I stress, must be the only girl (10).

DOWN

2, 3. The other self lies dead (8).
4. You have a place in the Middle East for a farmer (6).
5. Horry Hutchinson turned into a 22-23 (15).
6. Bean on the carpet (6).
7. Pitted a gospel in a pocket edition, almost (10).
9. X has a beauty spot, the bad-tempered creature (5-5).
12. Luggage-van on the railroad (7-3).
13. Forward the Scots own to belong (7).
14. How summer should come, happily (7).
15. Lights of over 500 inches among dogs? (3-7).
19. Deeds of one inch, as above (6).
20. Cost about a quarter of a sovereign (6).
23. Account of legislation (4).
24. Spurs for 22s, maybe (4).

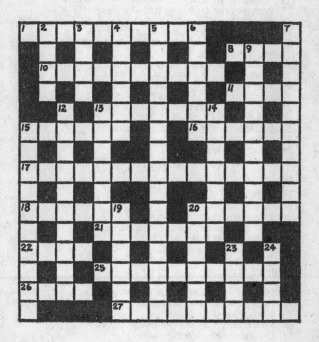

22

ACROSS

1. An expert on one bird or another (8).
5. No handicap to law-breakers to write badly (6).
9. Perhaps minister makes periodical payment about eleven? (8).
10. Looking scared when fencing? (6).
11. Makes me go to people in violent section of government (4, 10).
14. Deals that are penalised? (5).
15. Army in mire is retreating, in fact (5).
16. Was informed of a centre for cattle (5).
17. They might play in ways I despise (5).
20. Settled about cut in charge that's allowable (5).
22. Exaggerate aim? (4, 3, 4, 3).
24. Pressed to enter choir, one declines (6).
25. State of various lead goods (8).
26. He sounds serious (6).
27. As an after thought, changes the books (8).

DOWN

1. Pole raises point with artist (4).
2. Gift includes animal and musical instrument (7).
3. Shifty sort of country workers? (7).
4. Study a series, in effect (11).
6. Talked with many in Homburg, perhaps? (7).
7. Food meal from tin (7).
8. Lawful title involved with a sort of image (10).
12. Some of their interests are over our heads (11).
13. Party at which we might have a good deal to arrange? (5-5).
18. Soldier sees monster swallowing duck (7).
19. Dogs get place to rest, possibly (7).
20. Glib ale distributor gets a bit of cricket? (3-4).
21. A student enters a piece of work—music (7).
23. Favourites stand the pace (4).

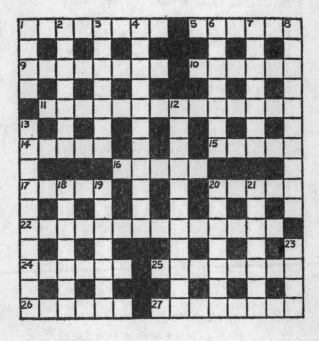

23

ACROSS

8. Cheerful artist? (8).
9. Out of tune; move or go out (6).
10. Reflective Italian woman at a nerve-racking reception (6).
11. Beyond one's control but, in fact, good (3, 2, 3).
12. Fairy uses a mathematical symbol without hesitation (4).
13. Comic strip about Omar and the ox-tail displays Socialist sympathies (3-7).
15. Once it's been analysed, have a slice (7).
16. Trade requirements? (4-3).
18. Dickens character is direct and forward (10).
19. This is a non-U word (4).
20. Packed, and strapped right in (8).
22. Rebuking the sailor? (6).
23. Wrinkled up bag has very little cash (6).
24. Continue briefly; the artist, by the way, is set in opposition (8).

DOWN

1. Timed to the last moment (3, 8, 4).
2. Home comfort for a parliamentarian? (1, 4, 2, 3, 5).
3. There's distinct evidence that many an old king quietly took cover (5, 5).
4. Betrayal of rate reform issue (7).
5. Shut up this house? (4).
6. What one is, and used to be, to project a Conservative image, needs no clarification (4-11).
7. Unresponsive state out over the headland (15).
14. A bird call interrupted by a bird, the same again (7, 3).
17. Prophesy to the prince, that's an order (7).
21. Writer with big ideas but without prejudice (4).

ACROSS

1. Nick's date leads to frustration (14).
9. Woman's swallowed poor Rene's port (9).
10. Conrad's work in early life? (5).
11. Run more? (5).
12. Outspoken quarrel in court, perhaps (9).
13. Meet tout out for a spin? (8).
14. Used to be a woman's ring (6).
17. Novel inclusion in one's Monday tasks (6).
19. May obscure view of fall? (8).
22. Seven anti-reform citizens (9).
24. Shows just a little sense? (5).
25. Dog returns bird to soldier (5).
26. Some brass parts in Ben's motor (9).
27. Adam and I? (3, 5, 6).

DOWN

1. Once more accented mounting immorality on board, perhaps (7-7).
2. Woman takes fragments of tile by pony (7).
3. Left publicity now broadcast in N. Ireland (9).
4. More than P.O. rules broken—about five (8).
5. Like breaking into poor Una's capital (6).
6. Might take article pertaining to ancient civilisation (5).
7. Feed rhino with us, possibly? (7).
8. Reading the alphabet, perhaps? (3, 5, 6).
15. Girl gets training on island climb—could be made fit (9).
16. Convivial suggestion for traveller? (8).
18. Ruler has time to carry on (7).
20. Agrees advantages are without point (7).
21. Affair appears to be of importance? (6).
23. If the criminal is found out? (5).

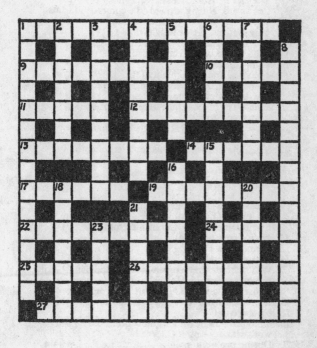

25

ACROSS

1. Are there others that are crazy? (6, 7).
8. 'Yes, they do' 's wrong for 24 (3, 7).
9. The city of Auld Reekie, very likely (4).
11. Cold water ebbing around 18's comrade at arms (8).
12. Tiny distance, great weight (6).
14. The French patron is at his study (5).
15. Rough mess round the river (5).
16. Tight for time? (5).
17. The same for more quality (5).
20. Mordant character reforming the tribe (5).
22. Thy love is perchance wanton (6).
23. Such was 12's 24 on the 19 of 5—not 8! (8).
25. Reforming 10 (4).
26. It's waxy in its turn about the hair-do on the card (10).
27. Stitch clothes with the national emblem (6, 7).

DOWN

1. Break the wash-stand in front of the Somerset exhibition (4, 3, 4, 4).
2, 3. Pub closed—take us outside from 18 (7, 7).
4. Native county? (6-4).
5. Premier river (4).
6. Waste of food? (7).
7. Waxy about what happens to the Muses just before twenty to eight (5, 6-4).
10. Those who do hope these will be 20 acrosses (4).
13. It's cut off from here and is in her itinerary (10).
18. 8's eponym (7).
19. '. . . . brought death into the world, and all our woe, with —— of 5' (12) (4).
20. During prohibition, how one reaches the junction (7).
21. What Neptune has delivered in canvas (7).
24. A relation in the city (4).

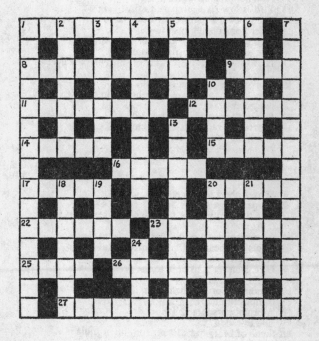

26

ACROSS

8. NCO changes line of talk (8).
9. Writer is back, we hear (6).
10. Ape new Indian fashion (6).
11. Bird is low-right-prepare to fire! (8).
12. Some poetical phrase for a similar river (4).
13. Offer lion cooked meat (6-4).
15. Soldiers are also included in scheme (7).
16. Wicked to take petrol in vessel? (7).
18. Nice bride roughly about fifty? Surpasses belief! (10).
19. Bank taken in by sailor? (4).
20. Poor mites must have a tea-break, in our judgement (8).
22. Has written one before two (6).
23. Sportsman ran with leg fracture (6).
24. The main rod used for fish (3-5).

DOWN

1. Why Robert took a cup? (3, 4, 4, 4).
2. Emperor is a sort of Hitler? Never a bit! (4, 3, 8).
3. Quietly tries scheme to outlaw ministers perhaps (10).
4. Composer has a point that's relevant (7).
5. Fools lose head and break into capital (4).
6. Aid to clearer writing (6-9).
7. OTC is never a trouble to the press, as a soldier might be (2, 6, 7).
14. Tending to prove michievous about one Dante composition (10).
17. A brutal person and a Roundhead coming in side by side (7).
21. Some of Margaret's letters turn up in India (4).

27

ACROSS

1. Publicity for bad actor in 15 across 18 (10).
8. Money whose head is in 15 across 18 (4).
10. A shilling and a penny for an African is 15 across 18 (10).
11. Loud performance, it's true (4).
13. Sea-lions return to a sign (7).
15, 18. The place for your Dutchman (6, 6).
16. Diana and others are taken aback (6).
17. Wire makes a play-goer dither (15).
18. See 15.
20. What can be learnt from the deer (6).
21. Equine irritation? (7).
22. Pity a girl that isn't finished! (4).
25 All the poor found in 15 across 18 (10).
26. Little boy in a whirl (4).
27. Caballer follows copper in 15 across 18 (10).

DOWN

2. '—— 11-0' (4).
3. German 23 that wasn't genuine (4).
4. Number 1 catch in New York (6).
5. Very good reception of very old joke? Another clue : he might roar (7, 8).
6. Suggested something for me to do (6).
7. Prove an actor to be a cricketer? (4, 6).
9. Original pupil? (5, 5).
12. Divide the country in 15 across 18 (10).
13. Empire couch? (7).
14. Flying high like this on a circle (7).
15. In a monopoly, the wood that has the grain (4-6).
19. Prowl round a painter without a bad name (6).
20. Pier of the cinema—old English? (6).
23. Small price for poison gas . . . (4).
24. . . . which could be a lot different (4).

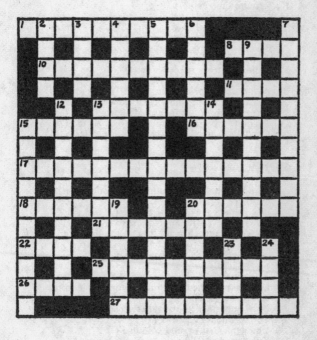

28

ACROSS

1. Bad time coming for the shop? (7, 2, 5).
9. Broach the gut? (7).
10. Require time in 3 (7).
11. Lamb's prophet (5).
12. Fine overheads? (4, 5).
13. Return pounds to the French cathedral like a slave (9).
14, 6. They take lumps out of bowls (5-5).
15. Follow in green suede shoes (5).
17. Loyal address in West Ham in 3 (9).
20. Associate of a trio and a grant? (1, 8).
22. Beast with a large number of women (5).
23. Information rather than cold sweets (7).
24. Bacon for the roast is supplied by Orlando (7).
25. Candour's directly between Scottish waters (14).

DOWN

1. Mendelssohn's contribution to sex education? (3, 4, 7).
2. The solitary may be one to rule (7).
3. Where to live with an awful shirker (9).
4. Backward French maid it takes the French to elevate (7).
5. Novel put under the ground in 3 (7).
6. See 14 across.
7. Study in 3 (7).
8. Let's take in one certain to doctor people in his spare time (7, 7).
14. Hard nuts cracked by soldier's leader in 3 (9).
16. Totters about musically (7).
17. Get copper, silver, and gold in 3 (7).
18. Ruler proverbially akin to the frying-pan (4, 3).
19. Bit of a horse marine, one that induces growth (7).
21. A Northerner in 3 (5).

29

ACROSS

1. Pigs' land in 19, 16 (8).
5. Contemporary object of search and symbolism (6).
9. Bridge between Yorkshire and London in 19, 16 (8).
10. Desk at the office (6).
11. Why touch? (5, 2, 7).
14. Means a chap (5).
15. The word for many a hooligan (5).
16. See 19.
17. All I give back includes a watch (5).
20. Fabulous article on how to sit back (5).
22. Quest for truth and falsehood? (7, 7).
24. Tea party in 19, 16 (6).
25. In various senses King George is in 19, 16 (8).
26. Country stories about Fawkes? (6).
27. Gold leaf with silver and copper in 19, 16 (8).

DOWN

1. Article of clothing in the window (4).
2. Fashionable American river taken from the French (1, 2, 4).
3. Skilful round—uncle's half dead! (7).
4. Arrows have a point on top—that's a close thing! (6, 5).
6. Just a trip, marshal! (7).
7. Laundry partly off 19, 16 (3, 4).
8. Run and get the cops in 19, 16 (10).
12. Pseudo-silver chalice shaking like corn (5-6).
13. What bites the churches in the autumn? (7-3).
18. My brig's wrecked in 19, 16 (7).
19, 16. Race for the president's other heir (12).
20. Island opposing half the Guards (7).
21. One of the poles to an Italian city (7).
23. Like an old car with a habit (4).

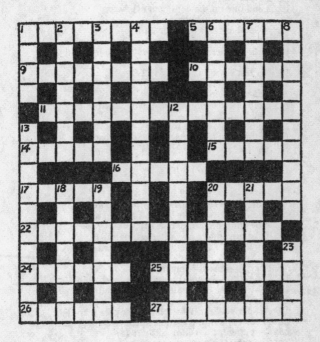

30

ACROSS

8. End of January all right? Oh, for a master 2! (8).
9. 2 Hold? (6).
10. 2 and one on the continent (4).
11. Another 10 in shorn 2 (10).
12. A Salic arrangement for 2 (6).
14. 2 severely rattled (8).
15. With the cleric around, we return to the field of 2 (7).
17. No test's good enough for 2 (2, 5).
20. 2 in front of hill in Iowa (8).
22. 2 lethal when seen? (6).
23. Gold, after being changed, is inclined to be 2 (3, 7).
24. Hand out 2 (4).
25. Plant drink on 2 (6).
26. Retrograde requirement regarding bachelor 2 (8).

DOWN

1. Base side of a boy? (4-4).
2. Now come round after tea—it's no rural retreat (4).
3. The fool is taken in by the French girls (6).
4. Not quite the same, old girl! (7).
5. Take advantage of winter estimates (8).
6. Innocent? The young imp has caused a landslide! (5, 5).
7. Stick to present company (6).
13. It's extra —— and I load it insecurely! (10).
16. When older, Len could be registered (8).
18. They're on the radio in Yorkshire (3, 5).
19. Article between two vehicles may be a trailer (7).
21. A certain admiral caught a fish and staggered (6).
22. Sent crazy, the editor settled! (6).
24. She achieved nothing (4).

31

ACROSS

7. Stately home or any other house in 11, 9 (5).
8. The endless strikes not backed in 11, 9 (9).
9. See 11.
10. Nearly put the kettle on the gas in 11, 9 (9).
12. Every personality takes the bait as Bunyan does (11).
16. Despair in the Pilgrim's Progress (4).
17. Rests at the lock (5).
18. See 21 (4).
19. Nobleman's nobleman get on in 11, 9 (5, 6).
22. Write music on two notes and disintegrate (9).
24. Retiring old bird gets near in 11, 9 (5).
25. 26s for students? (4-5).
26. It's 6 to be authoritative (5).

DOWN

1. Round piece of wood in our (split) Golden Bough, for example (9).
2. Propped up round number that's reduced (9).
3. Sounds scaring but can be downtrodden (4).
4. Stately home taken over by those who play the lead in 11, 9 (6, 5).
5. Steal something from someone? You surprise me! (5).
6. Going to the limit? (5).
11, 9. Region of 8 in Homer? (16).
13. One wood that's very good (5).
14. Apricot it may be for the country (9).
15. Somewhere to sit at the dance? That's not quite cricket! (9).
20. His borough is a 23 in 11, 9 (5).
21. With 18, direction of labour in 11, 9? (5).
23. The district sounds steep (4).

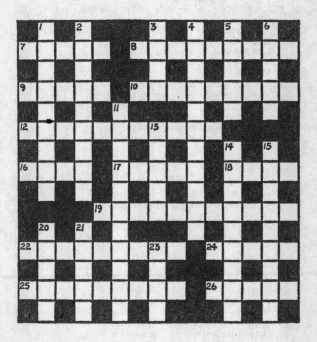

32

ACROSS

1. Obstruct the ground (10).
6. Lights of gold up in the air (6).
9. Characteristic of Burke's soldiery to strike a town (8).
10. Such societies presumably aren't reserved (8).
11. Watch the South gate (6).
12. Like the Roman country in 1 across (8).
14. Motor with a yarn in 1 across (8).
16. Replaced in an overture in 1 across (8).
19. Self-regarding cities go wrong (8).
21. Newspaper quotation for the mob (3-3).
22. Get through to a peer distracted about food (8).
23. Mozart aria by love-birds on love (4, 4).
24. Ascetic of limitless energy (6).
25. Effective weight in 1 across (10).

DOWN

1. Head man from council hall in 1 across (6).
2, 22 down. New model army takes wine in 1 across (8).
3. A threat of a snap? (8).
4. Characteristic of Burke's soldiery: insolence suits? (14).
5. A white note, fool! (7).
7. 'That —— which men miscall delight' (Shelley) (6).
8. Note—need key: wax to be moulded fairly soon (3, 3, 4, 4).
13. Sharp note in a card (5).
15. Yearn to win when I go in 1 across (8).
17. In Italy James can make magic rings (7).
18. Orkney leaders leave 25 in 1 across (6).
20. Irishman died with nothing in France (1, 5).
22. See 2.

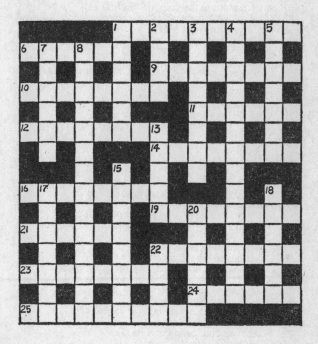

33

ACROSS

7. Inn, for example, supplying more than a gill (5).
8. State of 7 (9).
9. A sly remark to the point of 7 in Italy (5).
10. Middle East 7 the pauser disturbed (9).
12. Cars were out from 7 (11).
16. It details choices of 12 denied 7's make-up (4).
17. Learning about one French 7 (5).
18. Garden 7 (4).
19. Composer missing the point put into aria without one 5, 7 (11).
22. Tunny 7 in Cape Province (5, 4).
24. 7 (Scottish) girls sharing a letter (5).
25. Raise suet mess to 7 mouths (9).
26. Russian 7 achieving one gain in going (5).

DOWN

1. Saskatchewan 7 to discover afterwards (9).
2. Assessed the likely value of huge dip we organised (7, 2).
3. Country landscape, rural in part only (4).
4. One without these was upset oscillating in play (2, 3, 6).
5. A service return out east (5).
6. Directions to take to a German 7 (5).
11. Chisel-shaped token of victory for insertion in the border (11).
13. Male with an acceptable hair-do (5).
14. Opposing nag punter fixed (9).
15. Classify again the mountains at the back (9).
20. Set in order by habit (5).
21. 7 label you and me in Portugal (5).
23. Gasp, eyeing part of a Scottish 7 (4).

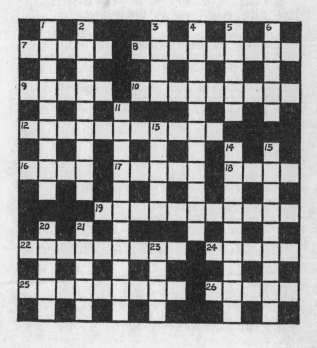

34

ACROSS

1. Why sloth and jargon spoil a novelist (4, 10).
8. Spirits of hydrogen, I imagine (5).
9. Cause another split in the left wing, I see (8).
11. Wind from the South and East on the stern (7).
12. Twist a bad hat: that's the way to fight! (7).
13. Give accommodation with the job? (3, 2).
15. Gibbon, for example—namely a 6 and 6 (9).
17. The mood of the moment about size—get it? (9).
20. Glutinous as a nail? (5).
21. No. 1 club for a prince? (4, 3).
23. Advocate of the sound of songs at the piano (7).
25. Slope to conceal troubles in (8).
26. Taxi home—just a little one (5).
27. Owner of 1 across (1, 3, 2, 8).

DOWN

1. A fitting pastime (6, 6).
2. County of Quorn and Pytchley, for example (5).
3. West African swine on trial (6-3).
4. A big ship, the Bounty! (7).
5. He's lost his wife with the marriage portion (7).
6. Down which there are sails or sales? (5).
7. Rich upper-class lady affected by liquor (9).
10. Liquor keeps her within call by hiding the source of gold (6, 6).
14. I for one enter half the trumpets in the church (9).
16. Goat with a prize flower (9).
18. Document arriving shortly (2, 5).
19. What the aristocracy wear in the car? (3, 4).
22. French settler: that's it! (5).
24. A false beard seems to be exclusive (5).

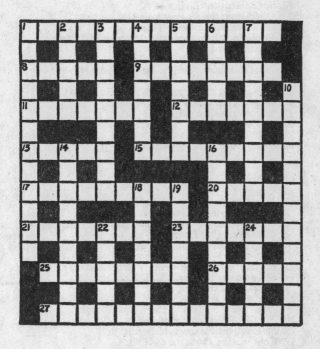

35

ACROSS

8. National 11 involving babes without exception (8).
9. Wine you returned in 11 (6).
10. Speak tartly in childish 11 (4).
11. Orient race given a new form (10).
12. Common association in 11 (6).
14. Example of how those who 24 across as 11 may differ (8).
15. Entomological 11 (7).
17. Point to a lumberman, one laying about him at 15 (7).
20. String along round part of Scotland as 11 (8).
22. It has its ups and downs in 11 (6).
23. Indirect means of 11 (10).
24. Beat back as 11 (4).
25. A wrinkle used in 15 (6).
26. Make music about select 11 (8).

DOWN

1. 15 blocker, a farm-steadying feature (4-4).
2. Spring in fashionable apparel (4).
3. 'You shall be yet far —— than you are' (All's Well That Ends Well) (6).
4. Limp leather brought back by the hero (7).
5. You, as the Spanish art supporter (3, 5).
6. Geometrically-minded American's comment on an appealing invader? (5, 5).
7. Courageous verse (6).
13. Canon Eric and I adapted in a certain classical style (10).
16. Even lads become dominated (8).
18. Making possible inn gable repair (8).
19. Contribution about the code (7).
21. Afloat with something often used in 11 (6).
22. Arranged to depart (3, 3).
24. Take in the bird (4).

36

ACROSS

8. Bode ill—it's nearly 3.10 (8).
9. In a 23 at inattention (6).
10. The vulgar idea of bronchitis (6).
11. It's horizontal here in the French game (8).
12. Kiss one who didn't feel Cupid's darts (4).
13. No dish ever could be spoilt by cream (10).
15. The second spring of a young man's fancy? (7).
16. Rikki-Tikki's tail's in the morning for 2 (7).
18. Can't one speak thus with one's sleeves rolled up? (3, 3, 4).
19. Home for machine-guns (4).
20. Is love an encouragement of like tension? (8).
22. The route is immaterial (6).
23. Moderate mood (6).
24. Current utilitarian people (4-4).

DOWN

1. Schoolmaster's Christchurch? It fell (3, 5, 2, 5).
2. Throwback wanted to transcribe what the Sappers say happened (9, 2, 4).
3. What to dance—and when? (10).
4. When topless birds wash they are enthralling (7).
5. Birds starting to be smart (4).
6. It was turned by Ahab's envy into a dud cheque (7, 8).
7. The line of very few ohms (5, 10).
14. To be registered? Not if one gets clever! (10).
17. Emerge in effect (7).
21. Can or may be the rule (4).

ACROSS

8. Projector takes part with the rest, possibly (8).
9. Way affectations are put to flight? (6).
10. River smell, say? (4).
11. Noble is abroad—now to resettle in Lancashire (10).
12. Bob should be looked for (6).
14. Man meets women of the islands (8).
15. Things put on the back of ancient songs and pieces (7).
17. Native Belgian settler (7).
20. Plentiful materials for sailor and foreign worker (8).
22. Girl I'm backing to write a book (6).
23. Rome's role's about to change (4, 2, 4).
24. Unpleasant feeling of treachery (4).
25. Mark takes sailor a gem (6).
26. Features include ale-brewing natives (8).

DOWN

1. Sound fuel, of course (8).
2. Clothes changed for climbing? (4).
3. Declare, like The Rest, possibly? (6).
4. Sailor and many in cast appear stiff (7).
5. Bless me, a clumsy building to put together! (8).
6. Some crests of certain birds (10).
7. Desultorily read features of speech (6).
13. Fresh earth collected from the wood (5-5).
16. Harangue confuses Ida before the race (8).
18. Hatred of a lean record-breaker (8).
19. Extend imprisonment, some say (7).
21. Blockhead has fish to open up (6).
22. Food that is supplied by the club (6).
24. Space to stand for a time (4).

ACROSS

9, 10, 21 across. Celebrated engagement problem confronting the middle-aged? (3, 6, 2, 3, 5).
11. New trap setting threatened during 9, 10, 21 across (7).
12. Some resign or edge out when set aside (7).
13. A sharp edge in the 'ebrides (5).
14. All these I embrace triumphant in 9, 10, 21 across (3, 6).
16. Global location of 9, 10, 21 across, area one put there possibly (8, 7).
19. Proposed scrambled eggs in suet mixture at day's commencement (9).
21. See 9.
22. Ragout done to a rich turn (7).
23. Hebrews engaged in grave, explosive subject (3, 4).
24. Saw a girl, say, by arrangement (5).
25. 20 Leader in 9, 10, 21 across (9).

DOWN

1. As target is being dismantled copy dodges (10).
2. Gambler turn and amorphously turn about (8).
3. Easy catches according to the onlookers (6).
4. Block the way to work (4).
5. As to disorderly meeting dunderhead gets organised (10).
6. County light correctly sited (4, 4).
7. Pianist all but overcome about Rachmaninov's first in 11 (6).
8. 5 object to a sale (4).
14. Pamphleteers start Arcot rebellion (10).
15. The foundation or base to tree (10).
17. Variety of pear dear abroad to the cleric (8).
18. Edward's let in, suitably greased (8).
20. National composer (6).
21. Take in the animal and mount (6).
22, 23. He ran set otherwise and boosts morale (8).

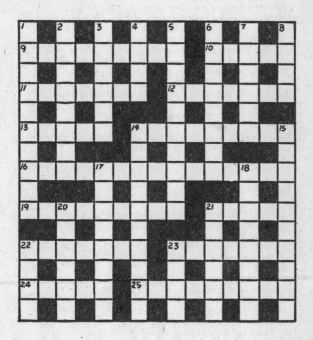

39

ACROSS

4. With authority in charge one is surrounded by waste (8).
8. Able to copy a savoury (6).
9. As some clergy are anti-State leadership in a way, or the reverse? (8).
10. Rake unwilling to come to a foreign river (8).
11. One Denis, out? Not out! (6).
12. Average weapon, in a manner of speaking (8).
13. Unit of government, not without love (8).
16. Crash about if you start back like a lobster! (8).
19. Able to qualify point with confounded glib lie (8).
21. Rise of a smell (6).
23. Some point rude remarks about his coming uninvited (8).
24. Offend gravely at first, then again—gaol! (4-4).
25. Threaten people with one (6).
26. He is sick, but he won't be examined (8).

DOWN

1. Vessel starts moving on German river (7).
2. Medical study makes Saint shortly go up into holy place (9).
3. Biblical location referred to by the Brontës (6)
4. Excess indulged in by cox? (3, 4, 3, 5).
5. This bird is a flaming duck (8).
6. This cut is enough to lay bare the skin (5).
7. Forsake a company —— numbers up (7).
14. Foreign John and Mary about to go to pot (9).
15. Regional dictatorship begins with rigorous following (8).
17. Stay, but note malice (7).
18. Uncle somehow taken in falsely, first and last by smoothness of tongue (7).
20. Not too late; one point, it's up to me (2, 4).
22. Keen, but shows hesitation about age (5).

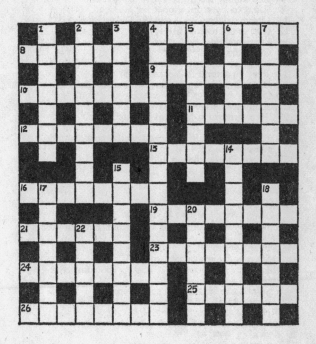

40

ACROSS

1. Against cash allowance essential for student? (13).
8. Idle money led up to breakdown (10).
9. Right to interrupt a poet for a second? (4).
11. Opera makes a hit—Noel is the producer (8).
12. Girl gets the same fish (6).
14. Poet remains in quarters (5).
15. Clear the land? (5).
16. Song for the piano's maltreated (5)
17. Rent no retreat in Yorkshire (5).
20. Dressed up instantly for part of Poe's detective (5).
22. A number set out to give opinions (6).
23. Two writers on the bank counter? (3-5).
25. Nasty look for king, say? (4).
26. He is thoroughly proficient in the new stamp rates (10).
27. Fabric Stan collected adds to disorder in the barracks? (9, 4).

DOWN

1. Belloc's work might be read from Yucatan to Israel (10, 5).
2. Eyed rocks? (7).
3. Stretch of river vessels enter (7).
4. Take the odd pot-shot at East in the bathroom? (5-5).
5. Some have rare curios to declare (4).
6. Parts of Iran without a vehicle—heaven to some! (7).
7. Possibly annoyed Mrs West also, having to yield (3, 4, 4).
10. Give money quietly, of course (4).
13. Gin mixed in satisfactory fashion for the Duke (10).
18. Our betters on the river? (7).
19. Money for writing? (4).
20. Oxen in folds, perhaps? Just the reverse! (7).
21. Permit to put in head in the studio perhaps (7).
24. Patient boxer? (4).

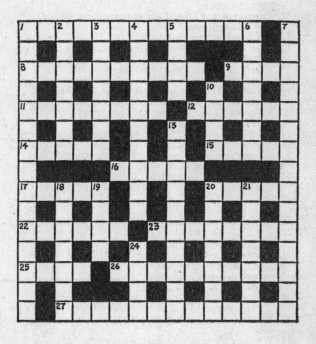

41

ACROSS

1. Ad hoc arrangement for one in Paris: that should be exciting (11).
8. Spare loaf (4).
10. Preserve of the French railway system: a number of light supporters (10).
11. Peace in our time! (4).
14. High key in the altogether that reminds me (5).
15. Advanced in a meal (6).
17. Thirsty inclination on the playing-fields of Eton (3-3).
19. Minor royalty, reduced to extremes, sold one to the Queen; one took her shilling (8-7).
20. Refractory type of elk embodies a type of dog (6).
22. Keen on leaving part of Sussex (6).
23. Blast those dogs! Do you hear them? (5).
24. They are opposed to us in the main (4).
27. Cut the quota? It's already on a shoe-string! (10).
28. The mark of one's profession (4).
29. Escutcheon of the dead bearing the taste of ashes (11).

DOWN

2. Oberon's familiar with the ice (4).
3. Homunculus is borne by the father: untrue (4).
4. Sheridan wrote in the third person (6).
5. Order 19s are prone to hear? (5, 2, 4, 4).
6. 'Done!' some say, to a gulosity (6).
7. Reflect, respect—take note—revile (11).
9. It's brought up to cut off the retreat (10).
12. Yes! A singing arab gets up to marry about four (11).
13. What the Vicar of Bray gained before catalysis (10).
16. Impeccable figures (5).
18. Commander helps to keep one going straight (5).
21. Queen Alice consumed with delight (6).
22. Obtain fifty per cent interest (6).
25. Miss 19 on both sides (4).
26. Concerning church prior (4).

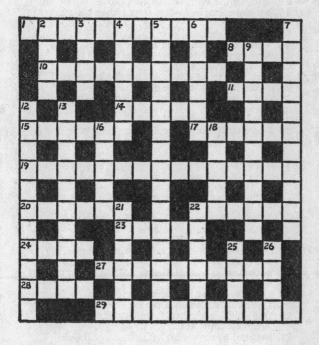

42

ACROSS

1, 5. K.L.M. pilot? (6, 8).
9. Refutation—copper is quiet on a roof (8).
10. Without the West Wind I turn almost purple (6).
11. No work, emphasised in return gives little help (7-5).
13. See 2.
14. Vision that's positive in 8 (8).
17. Art expressing the absolutely extreme (8).
18, 22. The Whale (4, 4).
20. Such as never attained what gentlemen prefer (5-7).
23. Taken from Candlemas to Lent (6).
24. One gets port in a society concerned with pressure lines (8).
25. A splendid issue? (8).
26. Notoriously wordy people (6).

DOWN

2, 13. Deposited as instructed (4, 4).
3. Without study I'm purple in the cheek, as they say (9).
4. Magazine that's mostly unprofitable? (6).
5. After I find one it would be telling (15).
6. It's unlucky down here (8).
7. Summonsed for being caught with a duplicate key (3, 2).
8. Article on hop-production in a world unfavourable to us (10).
12. Can't he expand his business? (10).
15. I made time without delay (9).
16. One liquid in another. I suppose (8).
19. Alcoholic firm? (6).
21. Material by name only? (5).
22. See 18.

43

ACROSS

1. Wave of support given to Shaw producer (8).
5. Dog had broken plant (6).
9. Settled a way to get round the mountains (8).
10. Part of Tunis; one hears, in which people may sing (6).
11. Deplore a break of service (8).
12. State one's real disposition (6).
14. Article congratulating people for entering certain compacts (10).
18. Fish with a nice blend of cleverness (10).
22. Result of letting some children talk (6).
23. Stake run through animal (8).
24. Mathematician finds new clue to instinctive forces (6).
25. Light thread? (8).
26. They would play one double (6).
27. Gives time to fire? (8).

DOWN

1. Wood does a bit of business? (6).
2. See artist about horse's head in metal (6).
3. Perhaps Chinese and the French use tricky methods (6).
4. Woman is to call to get meat in Norfolk (10).
6. Good-looking joiners in the house? (8).
7. Scorns the devil and is reformed (8).
8. Turner appears to take girl's breath away! (8).
13. Let McRae in for variation of trade (10).
15. Takes energy to load tree in Denbighshire (8).
16. Boxes the compass (8).
17. A trifle irritating? (4-4).
19. Perhaps a witch and her passenger take direction (6).
20. Annoy animals too—not ducks (6).
21. Landlord, in a word? (6).

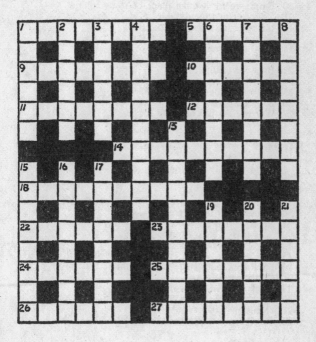

44

ACROSS

1, 5. 10 in 22 (Pair-royal?) (8; 6).
9. Cricketer resolved to lose girth (Not I!) (5-3).
10. Employment in quiet place of study (6).
11. Young trees roughly akin to logs (8).
12. Informer identifies old coin (6).
14. Guard chin without a 5 (5-5).
18. Used on some 2? (6-4).
22. Boxer, one of the great 23 (6).
23. IOU for example? (8).
24. Hornet variety that long absorbed 1 across (6).
25. An opportune banger? (4-4).
26. Bagpipe parts for lazy fellows (6).
27. Weighty feature of some 2 (8).

DOWN

1. 5 is 1 on analysing foresight (6).
2. A number jams hose markings (6).
3. Hold good gain (6).
4. Characters go on mixing with his padre (10).
6. Sound effect from some 2 (4, 4).
7. Final in half 25 (8).
8. Scot gets a bark from a tree (8).
13. Clans' ideas produce shock (10).
15. The goddess within is old and detached (8).
16. So Racine constructed the dramatic framework (8).
17. Declare girl is overweight (8).
19. Note, I go first to a Biblical land (6).
20. Occasional chance (6).
21. Regard some drivers—tee master-strokes (6).

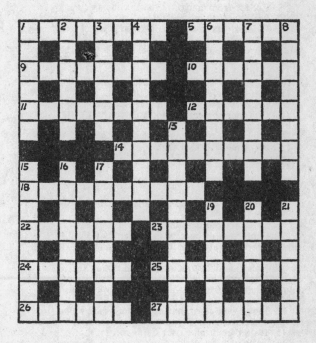

45

ACROSS

1. Sets of letters with points in common (15).
8. Its girth must be adjusted on one side (8).
9. Collect from uncle? Think again! (6).
10. Seats for comments? (8).
11. Worker gets some work back in place of union (6).
13. Novel sort of thinker, Owl! (10).
16. Speak too highly of the River Po joining the sea (10).
19. Untruthful article on magical priest (6).
20. Not all there at the Oval? (8).
21. Cockney protagonist has a convulsion: lovely! (6).
22. Give punishment in modern university accommodation by the sound of it (8).
23. As a result of one outburst, sanity seems not to be the genuine article (15).

DOWN

1. Dignity in divinity: Scotsman on what is owed to the loch (15).
2. Look of consideration (6).
3. Imply it must be kept in the family (6).
4. Die when about to return for example in the alley (10).
5. Hair raised by unconventional action (8).
6. Obviously not a self-made man (8).
7. Kindly return my shilling, by the way, and I start to call you names (15).
12. Liquefying agent, having a penny, isn't broke (10).
14. Male accountant requires a grave sacrifice (8).
15. It's a pair turning over the buzzers (8).
17. Religious instruction for a singer in Venice (6).
18. Whence Ulysses came in with a captive (6).

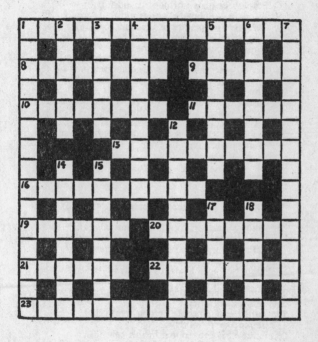

46

ACROSS

1. Arrive with space traveller—had no trouble (4, 2, 4).
6. Employees on a northern island (6).
9. In one way, Dowson writes most austere . . . (8).
10. . . . poems—lots tire of their intricacy (8).
11. Men of religion sound inquisitve (6).
12. Non-sober elements in Paris? (8).
14. When empty characters might foregather? (4-4).
16. Excuse everything one writes in a pet, possibly (8).
19. One of twelve anathematised by Hood (8).
21. Aim straight? (6).
22. Casual friend takes serious view of anthologist (8).
23. By the coast in Worcestershire? (8).
24. Scanty supply of shilling pears, possibly (6).
25. Thames duck is puzzled about another river —untravelled type (4-2-4).

DOWN

1. V.C. near parts where Clementine was? (6).
2. Gather for the service? (4).
3. Actor writes article—takes unusual pains (8).
4. Letters from Armenia that ire a queen (9, 5).
5. Remedy for having no pound notes? (7).
7. Lake holds river fish (6).
8. Supporter goes to dance on island—given by club, perhaps (8, 6).
13. Some of them denied taking foreign port (5).
15. Call for the letters? (4, 4).
17. Settled about people getting food (7).
18. Bookmakers' holidays? (6).
20. Farewell is interrupted in this case (6).
22. Some hopes of getting foreign currency! (4).

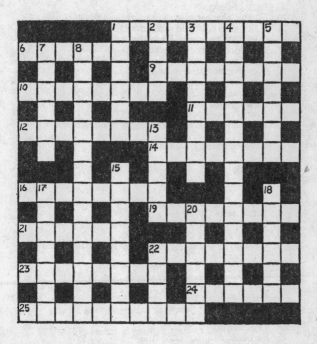

47

ACROSS

1. Method of producing industrial plant? . . . (7, 7).
9. . . . in the battery those chosen went on horseback . . . (9).
10. . . . this charger gives 11 power . . . (5).
11. . . . bonus offered in next race (5).
12. A lock turns no one back, that's positive (9).
13. Third order, try out, inertia (8).
14. Let Maud off without a penny—it's charming! (6).
17. Carry on with the summary (6).
19. Artificer without a plan is frightening! (8).
22. There and back—not straight back, surely? (5, 4).
24. Vehicle, old, finally gone for a song (5).
25. Not so risky—fears misplaced (5).
26. To place of worship—nothing in it but an image (5, 4).
27. Vessel currently on the boil (8, 6).

DOWN

1. Business is private—but at liberty to go in and purchase (4, 10).
2. City street is in comfort (7).
3. Banishment, or casts 'im out (9).
4. Heartlessly put up the money on Roundhead in any volunteer unit (8).
5. Not partial to a few lines? (6).
6. One grasping motorway service loses grip (5).
7. The French female has it, turning up on the first night—setback for the marriage! (7).
8. Place directed entirely to logic—nothing lacking (7, 7).
15. More arrived to start bathing in resort (9).
16. Of foreign topics, revolution is absolutely oppressive (8).
18. So up comes Lulu, loud in appealing to the emotions (7).
20. Old city company in substantial covering (3, 4).
21. One speaks at or before—or after (6).
23. Greek in Greenland or Iceland? (5).

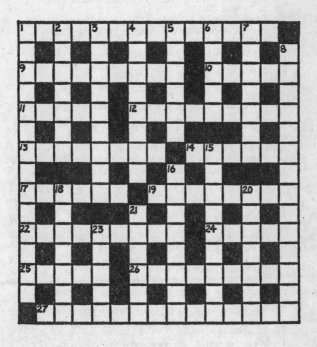

48

ACROSS

1. Picnic fare for the untouchable? (4-6, 3).
9. Beginning of 10 across or of 20 in the same place in the cast (7).
10. Strange sites in the chapel (7).
11. Roman coin—over two thousand pounds—found by Villa (5).
12. See how long the music lasts? (9).
13. A brilliant explanation (5).
15. Port gives mother a bad character . . . (9).
17. . . . and diverts the stream by appropriate means (9).
18. The British princess, not the American governor (5).
19. Leo is bull? Don't say such things! (9).
22. Paper rope on the bed (5).
23. Does he stock stocks? (7).
24. Battle finds the Sappers among the fruit (7).
25. Government security seems to require a successor to Jim and Roy (9, 4).

DOWN

1. After power: is about one thousand sufficient? (9).
3. Stoop among rude, ignorant folk (5).
4. Revulsion in the Old Testament is a must (5).
5. Go as the paper said? (9).
6. Grasp the point of stomach-ache? (5).
7. Turning up unexpectedly shows regalia's false (2, 5, 2, 4).
8. Resolve to stop the motorway race (13).
10. A sign for Thomas, the member for Surrey (7).
14. Egotishtical? (9).
15. What the British soldier painted the town with? (7).
16. Pursue knowledge with a half-nelson at a friend's house (3-6).
20. Eleanor the unknown in New York? (5).
21. A number—round number—in battle (5).
22. Clean the bush (5).

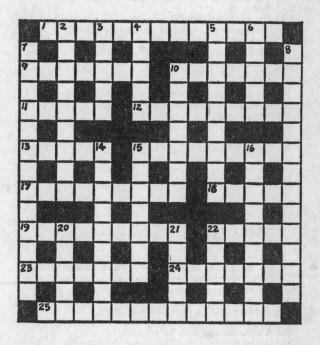

49

ACROSS

7. Are they driven hard? (5).
8. It is assumed to become unconscious eventually (5-4).
9. City of the classics (5).
10. Famous naturalist writes on lure for fish (9).
12. Mark takes gold into branch in Yorkshire (11).
16. Tip to get some cash in the bank! (4).
17. Browning girl joins a gentle Dickens boy—retiring type (5).
18. Object to letter written also (4).
19. Put on a board of some form in Paris? (6, 5).
22. Writers in no ways evil, possibly (9).
24. Scholar in desert in Morocco (5).
25. Emperor's wife gets the same stew about 7, possibly (9).
26. Greek physician from Gateshead—lean type (5).

DOWN

1. Gripping parts of the writer's work? (5-4).
2. Complicated package turns up, so to speak (9).
3. Burn I thought part of river (4).
4. They might be taken to represent certain groups (11).
5. Cleans and fillets bass without direction (5).
6, 11. Book a penny place if provided with change (5, 11).
13. Artist is content with a poor pension (5).
14. Just a passage we can translate immediately (5, 4).
15. Are they going to pot a duck on part of the roof? (3, 6).
20. A little surplus cash for port (5).
21. Kingsley's work is still about a shilling (5).
23. Look after the pence? (4).

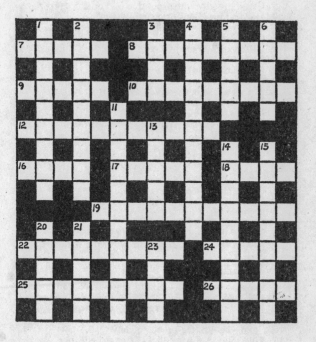

ACROSS

1. Pet? (See 12) (2, 4).
5, 26. 8 hero smells hock (Sort that one out!) (8, 6).
9. Claim proudly with aspiration in Yorkshire (8).
10. Hot feature of uniform circulation (6).
11. As to management, still being considered (2, 3, 7).
13. ——? (4).
14. Dissension about right piece (8).
17. Sort of hill mass—not very big (8).
18. Patriot count (4).
20. Falling off going downhill (2, 3, 7).
23. Towns a doctor restored (see 12) (6).
24. Heinous disorder leads to direction on how schools may be organised (2, 6).
25. Look at the minx! What a spectacle! (3-5).
26. See 5 across (6).

DOWN

2. Place for vehicle to reverse into (4).
3. Easily moved book is returned to island by a beginner (9).
4. Land includes I in truth (6).
5. Spot of trouble for 5 across 26 (5, 2, 3, 5).
6. Slip up and get the ring in to us for the wedding (8).
7. Flower in conflict occasionally with 5 across 26 (5).
8. Lady on being knocked into shape to confound author (5, 5).
12, 1, 23. Five across 26's recurring comment—simple! (10, 2, 4, 6).
15. Child—he was fed up completely (2, 3, 4).
16. Ride round the tribe about arrangement for removal (8).
19. A 14 of height (6).
21. Push around without a summons (3, 2).
22. Some ascribe detachment to a historian (4).

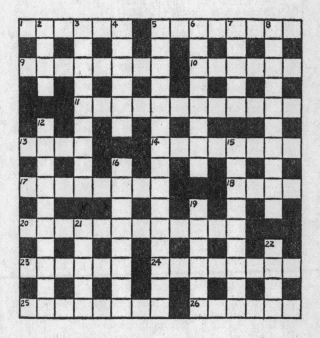

51

ACROSS

1. Retired doctor's got round the ship-builders' specious argument (7).
5. Horseback tour beginning for reformer (7).
9. Broke rib in morning—full of it! (5).
10. Five rugs and a chop in the train? (6, 3).
11. Arid letters still written about one's political creed (10).
12. Burning to get settled? (4).
14. It may make a significant change in the laboratory (6, 5).
18. Reading of some service in primary education? (5, 6).
21. Every one in the teaching profession (4).
22. Capital measures for cattle accommodation (5-5).
25. Perhaps a police physician works to provide sweets (4, 5).
26. Think of nothing long? (5).
27. Crescent-shaped ornament for musical instrument—catch in this! (7).
28. Conceals hill features round the north (7).

DOWN

1. Perhaps flight includes landing (6).
2. Show father, poor dear! (6).
3. Pure alum, etc.—am I to mix it? (10).
4. Doctor has to pull up for Baber's follower (5).
5. Hussars, hussars of the establishment, cut to ribbons (9).
6. In short, county flower producers? (4).
7. The corresponding case? (8).
8. I rent T.U.C. building, that's the solution (8).
13. Chambers upholds small buyer in Durham (10).
15. Majority of two to one (6-3).
16. Still last? (5, 3).
17. Tale about redhead causes disagreement (8).
19. Concerning climbing men one fitted with fur (6).
20. Basket-makers get very large rise, possibly (6).
23. Suits the patients? (5).
24. Arrange to take up some bright ideas (4).

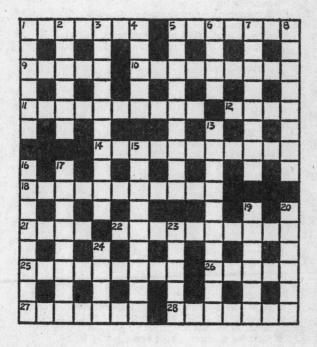

52

ACROSS

1. Biography of a one-eyed Irishman written in 1 down (3, 4, 2, 5).
9. Funny to behold: preservationists take one hundred (9).
10. Someone growing in a state of oppression (5).
11. Saw time and time again (5).
12. Passage of the chosen through Jerusalem (9).
13. Four-fifths of a lustrum were spent in Greece (8).
14. Burn in France, and rather more than a burn in Hants (6).
17. Learning to assimilate a hot-head in the sub-continent (6).
19. Given up voting for the repeater on the mount? (5-3).
22. Anonymous types cut and sharpen; and one is soundly beaten (9).
24. Escape that escapologist dislikes (5).
25. He interprets the law in the same place, to lawyers' abjuration (5).
26. One's punctual, discriminative, and extemporaneous (9).
27. C-c-c-clot! (9, 5).

DOWN

1. Mammon's circuit? (3, 3, 2, 6).
2. Having yen about art of self-control (7).
3. A warden in Chancery? (3-6).
4. Former Italian and Roman king, we can conclude, went to pot (8).
5. Simple physiognomy with a Latin infusion . . . (6).
6. . . . infusion iconoclastic Greek rejected (5).
7. Potter's speech (7).
8. Suffering Kismet! It's got whiskers on it! (4, 2, 4, 4).
15. Toc H mob disperses to a head-examiner (5-4).
16. Delicate forfeits for double-entendre (4-4).
18. Henry I had an objection to fish (7).
20. Prepare to arrive at . . . (3, 2, 2).
21. . . . an expression of Homeric laughter (6).
23. Classical king, one with the carriage of a child? (5).

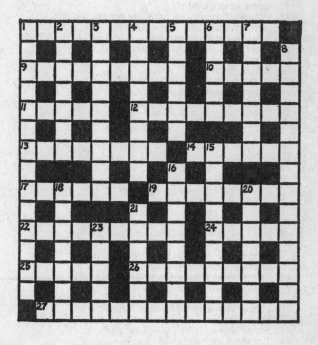

53

ACROSS

9. Rather slow housekeeper for the Jewish quarter (9).
10. Tickle one of nine (5).
11. Local advertisement? (3, 4).
12. Catspaw for small cat, often in boot (4, 3).
13. Number with remainder of 23 across, perhaps (5).
14. Briar rather than clay at the camp fire? (4, 5).
16. Trent scholar may go to school (8, 7).
19. School discovered nigh a pump (9).
21. School game (5).
22. School a little way to the poles (7).
23. Maximum speed ahead? (7).
24. School in progress to Westminster (5).
25. Confusion of love with sex—page one—could be dynamite! (9).

DOWN

1. The party becomes calm and I dry up (5, 5).
2. Rio, an old city which was Rome (8).
3. Economy in the garden (6).
4. School that raises a sound (4).
5. Storm tempo? It isn't over quick (4, 6).
6. Insect entertaining a tailless rodent, and how they get on? (8).
7. 'Wandering voice' that 'mocks married men' (6).
8. Touched one's hat, perhaps (4).
14. School game cut short in cold weather (10).
15. Miniature writings used as eye-tests (10).
17. 'A hive for the ——' (Yeats) (5-3).
18. Muslin makes the instrument stop (8).
20. Captive internally sick in bed (6).
21. School that adds weight to acting (6).
22. Too short for others like this (4).
23. Model sort of character (4).

54

ACROSS

1, 5 across. Dairy 'plug': drink to the poet (7, 7).
9. Puzzled attitude towards a copper (5).
10. Celebrities trap rodent around Minehead in the cooler (See 16) (6, 3).
11. Odd service to found (10).
12. Dye found in the ocean, I learn (4).
14. Everything considered, where the fakir lies? (2, 3, 6).
18. Choice poetry anthology used by the printer (11).
21. Take in USA constellations (4).
22. Create (4, 2, 1, 3).
25. What the earl stands on or lives in (5, 4).
26. I do it differently but this is natural (5).
27. Triumphed around here: on what? (7).
28. Father circumvents the offer of a chair (3, 4).

DOWN

1. Fleet St half-ready to be shot (6).
2. Leave off. Hades! I stayed in (6).
3. A river, therefore, with more of the same kind (3, 2, 5).
4. He wrote of the French enemy (5).
5. 1 ac., 5 ac., character, a sort of rebel? Yes, without quarters in South Africa (9).
6. Drink up quickly? Stop (4).
7. Pervading 10, according to Mrs Malaprop? No chaps (8).
8. It's common knowledge Les is in the race. How soft! (8).
13. Treat the detail completely on the cricket pitch (5-5).
15. Ban? Yes, ten ban toil anyway (9).
16. '——19, 10' (1 ac. 4 ac.) (3, 2, 3).
17. File base if practicable (8).
19. Open forcibly without one good word (See 16) (6).
20. Was entangled with the wrapping (6).
23. Supports for strongholds (5).
24. The original barmaid? One of the best (4).

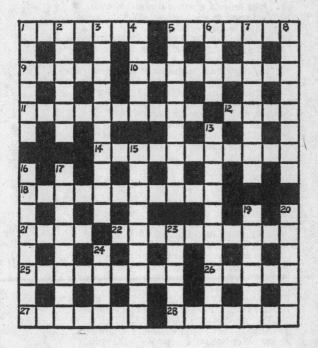

55

ACROSS

1. Lazy type—hugs girls—not right! (8).
5. Mark takes retired scholar a beetle (6).
9. Light on odd tree in Cardiganshire (8).
10. Dr Lane gets the weed out (6).
12. Put up in the Rectory? (5).
13. Preserve unusual cruets in certain solutions (9).
14. Bill and detectives tell any members, by some chance? (12).
18. Yielding Czech leader up to Italian irregulars (12).
21. Leave shortly before tea-break, without complaint, but appear unsteady (9).
23. Features of Blake's opening lines (5).
24. The main hero in Lancashire? (6).
25. Taxing affair, to beat time (8).
26. Puts on suede material without direction (6).
27. Make allowances for writers' charges (8).

DOWN

1. Metal of novel character (6).
2. Not suitable for nations to assemble (6).
3. Heavens!—is that Bruce? (5, 4).
4. It's a plant, of course, man! (5-7).
6. Sing in such anthems? (5).
7. Result of letting opening turn appear (4-4).
8. Inner contents appear sweet? (5-3).
11. Thorn's position, perhaps—in confidence (5, 3, 4).
15. Moor's bent on collecting musical instruments (9).
16. Cleanse hundreds standing on Geneva building (8).
17. The kind of band that Holmes investigated (8).
19. Try to shoot duck for food (6).
20. Animal goes round enclosure in trees (6).
22. 'O sweet Fancy! Let her ——' (Keats) (5).

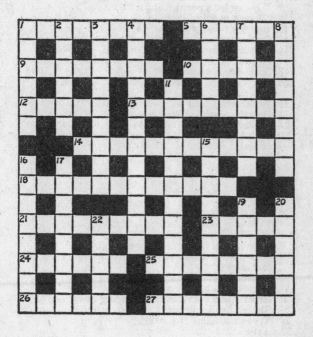

56

ACROSS

1. Made a bad stroke and got caught? (6).
5. Sees another meaning in remarks (8).
9. Weapon for a peevish salute? (8).
10. Surgeon of fifty tires badly (6).
11. Entire tax too oppressive, possibly (12).
13. Some chaps eat during recess (4).
14. Our cry—do renew the material (8).
17. Doctor's prescription for renewed strain? (5, 3).
18. Special food conference? (4).
20. Great man gets mistakenly praised in Pilgrim's Progress (5, 7).
23. Native gives little party—any cocktail? (6).
24. Half the pearls are Stevenson's (8).
25. White breaker seen on board? (3-5).
26. They happen to be still on the way back (6).

DOWN

2. Acquire some learning? (4).
3. Stale elements in Hardy character—insipid (9).
4. Society girl took courses—causes discussion (6).
5, 6. A way to put in a line in this crossword, possibly—from a hymn (6, 9, 8).
7. Offend again is the substance here (5).
8. Poles are the chosen people, so Red revolutionary concludes (10).
12. Valuing a quiet bit of commendation (10).
15. Stress being short of certain goods (9).
16. Joiner interrupts enthusiast to go and dance (8).
19. He includes one hundred out of spite (6).
21. Answers to name of poet (5).
22. Home note? (4).

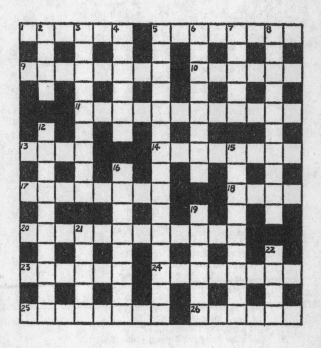

57

ACROSS

4. Companion for tea, in which some strike (8).
8. Nasty creatures in here? Never mind! (6).
9. Charles the Simple's about to buy (8).
10. Cataclysm literally visible at night (8).
11. Slight measures last month (6).
12. Germs are at work in Stalin's henchman (8).
13. Germs are in motion in the Lakes (8).
16. The gods long to get on with Man (8).
19. H—for example. Hook, perhaps (8).
21. Noises off in Cyprus (6).
23. One to a thousand and a thousand to one—that's freedom! (8).
24. Palace visible from the Balham branch (8).
25. Wonder how Slough gets publicity? (6).
26. Go forward or go back, right among the journalists (8).

DOWN

1. Crier who hunted in verse (7).
2. Bring an insect into the country—that's serious! (9).
3. Has he a corner in tall stories? (6).
4. Pen a signature as for pensioners (15).
5. Sort of comment on a sort of seat (8).
6. Mount for a man with a musket (5).
7. The slur on the American character? (7).
14. Underground number, the setter that sets the time (9).
15. Belief as eccentric as possible (8).
17. Abolish a king with a ring (7).
18. Rust ate away the height (7).
20. Spoils, we hear, with plain grass (6).
22. Old cast of speech (5).

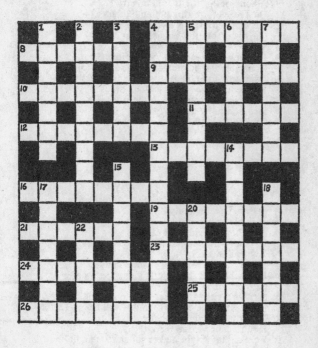

ACROSS

1. I have succeeded in a storm out of season (12).
8. It's inhabited by the habited (7).
9. A song on a shoe is inflationary (7).
11. Quiz master, or king with no defence (4-3).
12. His characteristic is to take gold (7).
13. Players before the English class (5).
14. When to be married shortly? (9).
16. Floating substance—bars of grime (9).
19. Constable the painter produces an oil (5).
21. I'm turning the blade, to put it incorrectly (7).
23. Happening to be rolling along? (2, 5).
24. Trout in the river, first in the front (7).
25. Demoralise by threats? (7).
26. Choose Roland and his sister for the resolution (12).

DOWN

1. Love in a wild genius is fiery (7).
2. Miss Ashford wasn't yet ready to make Mr Salteena gentlemanly (7).
3. Is liable to bloom (9).
4. How nice of Old Bill! (5).
5. Groundwork without a vestige of hesitation (7).
6. Jumped on a roof? (7).
7. He can spell kraits, for example (5-7).
10. Best behaviour means many changes among partners (5, 7).
15. Southern girl enters, her face in sacking (9).
17. Don't move the cream: trouble will follow (2, 5).
18. Quadrilateral and equilateral (7).
19. Don't acknowledge the girl! (7).
20. Roman playwright makes car start in addition (7).
22. One who owes a penny makes a settlement (5).

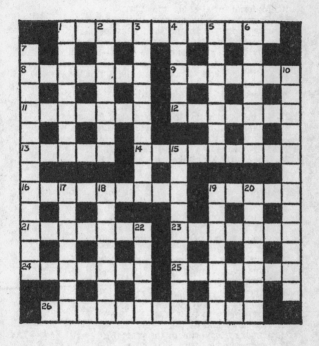

59

ACROSS

8. Rope from a pole? (8).
9. Wait and see a strange rite (6).
10. Material for a tennis dress? (4).
11. Solvent student has a portion to eat (6, 4).
12. Lowland: will all and sundry disclose it? (6).
14. Flower sound set in place of the little people (8).
15. Boy, Yorkshire opener, with coach—a small beetle (4-3).
17. A little tongue—a pound—in the top of the throat (7).
20. Everyone returns to take a degree from Evelyn Waugh's school (8).
22. Flying island may drink up most of the state (6).
23. Adam's climb affects all these answers initially (10).
24. Instrument that doesn't sound true (4).
25. Slave owner in a bottle-green coat (6).
26. The Swift? More likely the Milton (1, 7).

DOWN

1. Two eruptions in Pacific dress (4-4).
2. The king in Pygmalion (4).
3. Capital with a new start in Poland (6).
4. Sell tin of soup? (7).
5. It's all up with the girl I found in Wales (8).
6. Time to start smoking? (8-2).
7. Sheridan the writer (6).
13. Exposing by Algerian twists (6, 4).
16. Balanced but not quite set free (8).
18. It rarely has to be written (8).
19. Is a ball B and P? (7).
21. Forsake the North for the yeast (6).
22. Involve under fifty in a feeble way (6).
24. Ship's bottom up for Wales (4).

60

ACROSS

1. Coming in to carry away (8).
5. Spare about a bob at irregular intervals (6).
9. Band of engineers given directions—how mortifying! ... (8).
10. ... of feet, revoltingly sticky (6).
11. Sumptuous feed is nothing to us (8).
12. Strict way artist has with it (6).
14. Solicited and brought in about one continental (10).
18. Room for experiment with short left speech? (10).
22. The cunning about the thing is to stop (6).
23. Arrange first class tie-clip, obscuring the light (8).
24. Joined one with Edward shortly (6).
25. First class—right about initial trip; it's sealed (3-5).
26. Opening in point-to-point races perhaps (6).
27. Make more of a sincere construction (8).

DOWN

1. Nation begins to get old and contract (6).
2. Holding run-up; about to place for striking (6).
3. Consented to a possessive lust (6).
4. Study the total, comrade—perfect! (10).
6. Flat out—not right, it's a gland! (8).
7. Fires ran amok—curbs provided (8).
8. Smooth drift comes late in the day (8).
13. Company corner it somehow—for putting right (10).
15. Argument is certain to give enjoyment (8).
16. A bit over-organised, but it's fruitless (8).
17. Increasing number bob in lately (8).
19. Time of year when starting to bury (6).
20. Stain on character of corrupt, valueless magistrate (6).
21. Namely two articles mean injury (6).

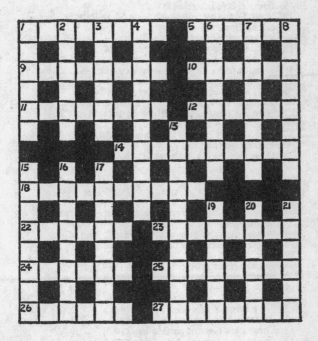

61

ACROSS

1. See 25.
5. Subjection of a hero of our time to time (7).
9. Being compassionate (5).
10. It retails the way in which little Scots join the establishment (5-4).
11. Time past for cobblers? (4, 6).
12. Unspecified a rejection in France? (4).
14. Hurt Edward and live madly by 25, 1 across (7, 4).
18. A snack at Edale prepared by 25, 1 across (5, 3, 3).
21. Volatile girl turns South: some girl! (4).
22. 25, 1 across concocted zero grades (6, 4).
25, 1 across. Of 9, 5; 7; 14; 18; 22 (We hold some heartless rôles gamut falls to an actor) (1, 8, 7).
26. Where film-stars strike? (5).
27. Primate king deserts French war, and two extremes retreat (7).
28. Daily many look hungrier (7).

DOWN

1. Blind borer holds Vietnamese leader—a boring business! (6).
2. Reveal man's inhumanity in Great Britain (6).
3. Unblemished record in hot surroundings, n'est'pas? (6, 4).
4. Animus, cant rejected: fly from the house! (5).
5. Must possibly be wet for a Whitehall infusion (4, 2, 3).
6. Alien entry evidently (4).
7. 25, 1 across's bloodless retreat (8).
8. Registers men's pale confusion (8).
13. Computers fashion ancient bead (10).
15. Greek in the main? No, Asian that is redesignated (6, 3).
16. A wit at the Milan opera? (8).
17. Throw a kiss and run to Winter Hill! (3-5).
19. Inventor raised without pretension (6).
20. A soothsayer with a sober heart—the dog! (6).
23. Stop tickling out of sight (5).
24. Celebration said to be worse than expiration (4).

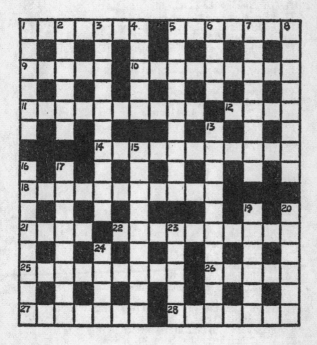

62

ACROSS

8. The creature sounds wet, darling (8).
9. Voiced by Chopin (6).
10. Claim support in drink (6).
11. Threatening the Left? (8).
12. Pale, after Bob got the bird (4).
13. Full orders for the poet following the clergyman (10).
15. Is it honesty to steal in sympathy? (7).
16. Pass, with undignified glee, a place of learning (7).
18. In the broken vat was an old clasp, people guarantee (10).
19. Reared British colour (4).
20. Rudiments of the weather? (8).
22. The District Attorney enters—for the better, until now (2, 4).
23. Quiet about puzzle (6).
24. Tender looks, how painful to see (4, 4).

DOWN

1. He goes along with one (6, 9).
2. A columbine, one on display very rarely (4, 2, 1, 4, 4).
3. At the height of excitement bring round a writhing viper (5, 5).
4. The cobbler's a saint (7).
5. Resort to northern stretch (4).
6. Family planning? (9, 6).
7. Longfellow's biographies of distinguished persons? (5, 2, 5, 3).
14. Tenor takes the way between two alternatives in modest literary work (5, 5).
17. Persevere with difficult rises when in training (7).
21. Want daughter: first-born (4).

63

ACROSS

9. Work to excess on this engagement? (9).
10. Something about wool gives protection from the cold (5).
11. Historian understood by you and me (7).
12. Fortification about which engineers lack confidence (7).
13. Canadian cannot make out a nymph (5).
14. Gaol-bird makes a break to Surrey town (9).
16. Customs may—with result in no doubt (4, 3, 4, 4).
19. For making alluvial deposits? (9).
21. Sloth is composer's ruin (5).
22. Road ran unevenly—what a state! (7).
23. End of Irish girl on the river (7).
24. Troopship ashamed to carry Eastern officer (5).
25. Going out, sergeant starts to turn in back row (9).

DOWN

1. Canvas not impermeable outside—that's ominous (10).
2. Penetrate? Not I!—I have, see! (8).
3. Prepared work for the galley slaves? (6).
4. Young lady is not much of a hit (4).
5. Noble is within rights, but they must be able to be seen (4, 6).
6. Region could be stew (4, 4).
7. Ground wherein lag starts short sentence (6).
8. Vessel right in to the left (4).
14. Rotten in French repeat German town (5-5).
15. Deceit acceptable to the lessee, officer! (10).
17. Steal up in a real cover of trees (8).
18. Legendary land—find it up north in Atlas (8).
20. Sidney got up in nutshell (and nothing else!) (6).
21. Listens to the point by which the body is carried (6)
22. Range about in display (4).
23. Tender about love's set-back (4).

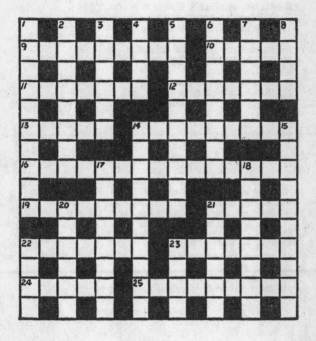

ACROSS

1. Capital ecstasy involving 1 down (6, 9).
8. They are not at home (8).
9. Stick at home, where we are (6).
10. Embarrassed at a Communist front? (3-5).
11. Painter one has to protect (6).
13. The minimum of litter, as it were, at Pontigny? (7, 3).
16. Parnell's non-nautical miles? (4, 6).
19. The student with a degree is a girl (6).
20. Calls over after all (8).
21. Honour is what W never does backwards (6).
22. Missiles aimed at two (8).
23. Policy statement complementary to 7? (3, 6, 6).

DOWN

1. Clue to 'Lime' as a station? (9, 6).
2. Modest conclusion to a game (2-4).
3. Slept in the open at some expense? (6).
4. Averted, not admitted (6, 4).
5. Having optimism in the blood? (8).
6. Reprove one for having gone too far? (8).
7. His Majesty isn't a foreigner (3, 5, 7).
12. Gorblimey! The debts of the ostrich! (10).
14. Decolonise? (8).
15. When sickness is about, a man of honour holds a torch (8).
17. Make conceited either way (4, 2).
18. Inner extremity (3, 3).

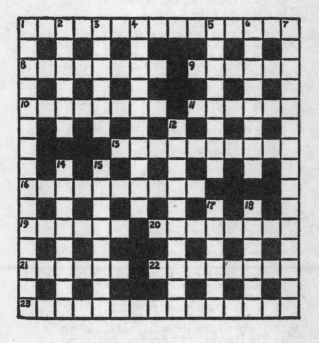

65

ACROSS

1. School association for sport (5, 6).
8. The order goes round: nothing may make a sound (4).
10. He comes from a land of airs and lives near Manchester (10).
11. Upper-class egg formation (4).
14. Learning to go back over the point to join up (5).
15. Necessitate being in late perhaps (6).
17. Lamb about to enjoin silence on a prophet (6).
19. He takes part in 1 across and sounds like an inexpert description of No. 2 in the boat (3, 6-3, 3).
20. Sea undergoes a change three times in this festival (6).
22. Is he against the queen? No, say the French! (6).
23. Lincoln supported by the French tree (5).
24. Variance may be a matter of course (4).
27. Codified legislation for getting the welt as taut as this (7, 3).
28. Journey a way through the woods (4).
29. Filling station expert on the rocks? (11).

DOWN

2. Bears the major part in high-level display (4).
3. Dance—in 1 across is not a round one (4).
4. He appears when one is in ill-natured company (6).
5. Enheartens lords to assemble for protection against attack from above (8, 7).
6. Can't? A world organisation can! (6).
7. Confining soldiers on manoeuvres? (11).
9. The bin-man's dismissal (10).
12. Where a 1 across man may pay homage? (6, 5).
13. The id's deepest configuration may appear precipitous (5-5).
16. She displays anger over a couple of points (5).
18. Licentious forward seen in 1 across behind 19 across (5).
21. Animal let out but kept in hand by one watching 1 across? (6).
22. Match number appertaining to hearth-goddess (6).
25. Flower may wilt (4).
26. Is indebted to us as subject getting so uppish about it (4).

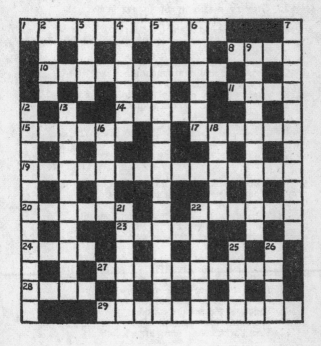

66

ACROSS

4. Trades and gives service—forceful in spasms (8).
8. Outcome of a lob from this end? (6).
9. Perhaps a note-case (8).
10. Growing possibility of an avalanche? (8).
11. Miracle rod—new materials (6).
12. River comes from the hill-crest (8).
13. Writer, and his novel to do with the country (8).
16. Warmer in Wales? (8).
19. Reject a possible double (4, 4).
21. Perhaps capital punishment is obsolete? (6).
23. Set out with one officer to collect rate (8).
24. Dress with some trouble on going to dance (8).
25. Poor Reade gets about a quarter—deserved the lot (6).
26. Condemn the writer's work? (8).

DOWN

1. Work at home upsets no one, in our judgement (7).
2. Woman gets direction to debar sort of religious offering (9).
3. Looked for rise of foreign renegades (6).
4. I am in it, and you are too! (3, 7, 5).
5. Right of presentation—a scholar promises to go into that (8).
6. Lifelong content for a wicked person! (5).
7. Change the washers? (7).
14. Badly rated for taking money on goods? (5, 4).
15. It might crush a white protector (3, 5).
17. Trade is on the turn and has mounted perhaps (7).
18. Bandages the cuts up outside (7).
20. Somewhat of a heart transplant for redhead (6).
22. Vessel with rising bow, little length (5).

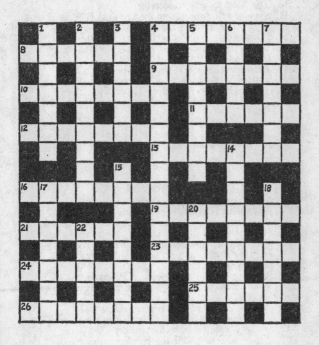

67

ACROSS

8. Odd gear sent round, with stripes (8).
9. Layer about, the beast! (6).
10. The food sounds reasonable (4).
11. Sex—what's done in for the criminal (10).
12. Number in tartan—that's cool! (6).
14. Court, foreign one in tribal setting (8).
15. To travel to and fro is clever? Nothing in it to thousands (7).
17. As upstart in mere pint-size, perhaps (7).
20. Soft in salesmanship, ordering letters (8).
22. Theologian surrounded by air of filth . . . (6).
23. . . . finishes article left about, covered with ants (10).
24. Pets can be a nuisance (4).
25. Sailor in bottom of boat, or in a nutshell (6).
26. He paints on the stage, in a way (8).

DOWN

1. Harem quarters lead to Gloria's ruin (8).
2. Age about usual to begin having illness (4).
3. Brutal mud-slinging, partly put into writings (6).
4. He runs when allowed in heat as arranged (7).
5. Face fine for obtaining drugs irregularly (8).
6. Held forth when copper is cantankerous about nothing (10).
7. Building erected to a deity in Pennsylvania (6).
13. Saint holding nothing against member is to make it up (10).
16. A ringlet changed into another shape (8).
18. Rat about those routed with varying resistance (8).
19. Shake a soldier over the gallery (7).
21. Bobby who strips off the skin? . . . (6).
22. . . . Bob takes mother round to see teacher (6).
24. Tart about soft instrument (4).

68

ACROSS

8. Pretend it's a mule? (8).
9. Preliminary to a bottle of rum (2-2-2).
10. Girl in drag at Harrow (6).
11. . . . most of whom, in the old song, is a rascal (8).
12. Change is of the essence in that case (2, 2).
13. City about to be vulgarly abased in ruins (6-4).
15. Almost imperceptibly vulgar round isn't clever (7).
16. Doctor has an attempt on a soldier (7).
18. 13 male's feather (10).
19. Remains out of sorts (4).
20. Horrid little bill for the carpet (4-4).
22. Dined at the pub, as is natural (6).
23. A crooked instrument? (6).
24. The animal with the stake has to stride out (8).

DOWN

1. The Gondoliers; or, relations go far round Brideshead at song (4, 2, 9).
2. Patience or, Dons in the rubber? (10, 5).
3. Dance which everyone on the volcano deserts when upset (10).
4. Ask Frost to put on some dirt? (7).
5. It sounds like a male song (4).
6. Thespis; or, The Gallery—awfully long word! (3, 4, 5, 3).
7. The Mikado; or, Top Ten if without alteration (3, 4, 2, 6).
14. Criminals in inter-class conflicts (10).
17. After a slip the bird fell (7).
21. Ought to marry for love? (4).

69

ACROSS

8. Paper-keeper (8).
9. Way noxious weed may be cooked (6).
10. Is the French for inch! (4).
11. I engage idolaters to produce leading articles (10).
12. Assimilate a summary (6).
14. Familiar hint (8).
15. Fast current (7).
17. Promote a loan (7).
20. The silt I trusted to form (8).
22. No avant-garde writer, by the sound of it (6).
23. It appears to turn quietly into a pair (10).
24. Inferior-sounding air (4).
25. The armament of a sound churchman (6).
26. Draws out chosen passages (8).

DOWN

1. The answer to it may be one quits! (8).
2. Not bound to be complimentary (4).
3. Turn aside to entertain (6).
4. Dull the way I spin around with my instinctive impulses (7).
5. Discordant score Ted accompanied (8).
6. Spiritualist seldom found a way to cook meat (6, 4).
7. French girl gets pill in training (6).
13. Provides amusement in harbours? (10).
16. Provides nourishment from triune form in New Testament (8).
18. Changes those who have changed their mind (8).
19. Yearned with despair (7).
21. Catching sight of revolting lapse I fall into (6).
22. A tense governing body (6).
24. Intend to put an article in the 'People' (4).

70

ACROSS

8, 9. These names make news! (8, 6).
10. Design for base? (4).
11. It isn't as he made out—just the opposite (10).
12. Song and dance connected with publicity (6).
14. He tests the tool, returning it to the worker (8).
15. Notice the airman in standard D? (7).
17. Risk meeting Lockhead in church? (7).
20. Flier looks about fifty (8).
22. Tell of altered treatment when penniless (6).
23. Birds alit by certain old scholars (10).
24. A second mark? (4).
25. Flavour of the time of year (6).
26. Hen spotted beetle? (8).

DOWN

1. Low sphere connected with game (8).
2. Made Norman part with port (4).
3. Life-line is available? (2, 4).
4. The hundred and second noise (7).
5. Would it be paid in marks? (4, 4).
6. Archbishop is to issue regular radio feature on climbing (4-6).
7. Punishment given to soldier? (6).
13. Mr Clay hoes in lugubrious fashion (10).
16. Ruling about double gin cocktail (8).
18. They tempt us with ten different refrigerators (8).
19. Mean elbowing West out of organisation? (7).
21. Connected with the craft of the farmer? (6).
22. Be in the house about eleven? (6).
24. Objection raised over a musical instrument (4).

71

ACROSS

9. Remove about one mile to north to prepare tea (9).
10. I love foreign artist but repulsed by the nose (5).
11. Opening 'Daily Express' will make dejected if not cross (7).
12. Keen listener at home (7).
13. To ramble sounds capital (4).
14. Town in Kent, of sole origination (10).
16. In the night, telephone rouses one—it's burdensome! (7).
17. Journey to some sort of oil port (7).
19. Gone off with one on table—it will pass (10).
22. Prepare to make an impression when the tide turns (4).
24. Taste mutton? That's puzzling! (7).
25. Prophet beheaded, one held to bring back his following (7).
26. With drink it's right to be on the lookout (5).
27. Past eight—but get cereal made up somehow! (9).

DOWN

1. Red Lion takes ten to cook a dish (10, 5).
2. Put out to gamble about (sic) up the mountains (8).
3. Women of strange views . . . (5).
4. . . . accommodation where man takes charge in ship . . . (8).
5. . . . below deck, not far down to dress up (6).
6. Of the Fathers, one St Patrick is most outstanding (9).
7. Related nothing about quarter of Spanish city (6).
8. Dreams of celestial 4? (7, 2, 3, 3).
15. Bill it to your first descendants (9).
17. Where one can pay one's way? (4, 4).
18. Speak about the noise—a sort of chord (8).
20. A bird—get round her, perhaps? (6).
21. Article mislaid about Maidenhead, nearly (6).
23. Irritating—it comes to many with not much hygiene (5).

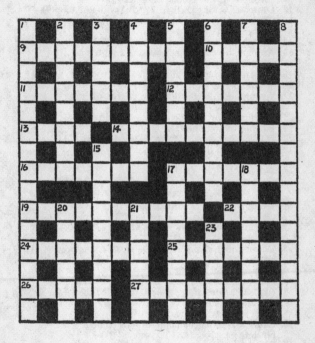

72

ACROSS

1. Held fast last month, returning without a light (7).
5. Clients needed the cut-out (7).
9. Set loose in the Home Counties (5).
10. Dramatic actor gets right backing with old Scot (9).
11. Commercial grower: names run round about the railway (10).
12. Hurt badly, a large number object (4).
14. Account of upper highway the country is giving point to (11).
18. For an anniversary glow? (6-5).
21. A girl to pity? (4).
22. Wrong admitted: student in charge of liquor store (3-7).
25. Blooming florin in debt to the Circle (9).
26. Balance of a pound (5).
27. Durable yet smart; from Latin America (7).
28. Mainly from the gallery (7).

DOWN

1. Keeps moving the church vases (6).
2. Covering the race in the river (6).
3. Promote skilfully, by choice (10).
4. Spotted—and cracked? (5).
5. Ocean-going chant about the east, a long way off (9).
6. Looks a point to affirm (4).
7. Many claim it is changeable, like the weather (8).
8. Explosive part of the globe, that's for me (4-4).
13. Fastidious individual? (10).
15. Fling it up, wildly cheering (9).
16. Derisive of science fiction, callous content gets a bit dull (8).
17. Oily appearance, uncouth almost to us (8).
19. Can't the French take on a French sailor? (6).
20. It's all up; Young Liberals must get out, shut up; what is left? (6).
23. Lawful support for others (5).
24. Each one a fairy (4).

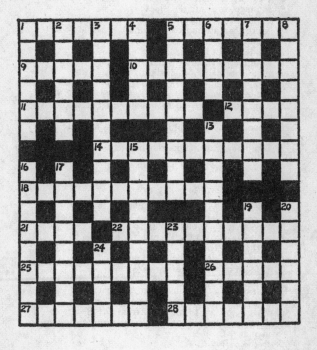

73

ACROSS

1. Perhaps Jack is in front, and Doctor Bill at back (4-4).
5. I'd more diversion—that's the word of course (6).
9. Manages to study the pipes (8).
10. Band tries arrangement without piano (6).
11. More than a hundred to a break, it might be assumed (8).
12. Model might be missed? (6).
14. Stimulating weather conditions? (6, 4).
18. Allude to loading cash getting priority (10).
22. General method might be made up (6).
23. Writes a novel on direction, so to speak (2, 2, 4).
24. More land given up to plough—first-class return (6).
25. Record artist in Kipling's work, in a measure (8).
26. Players in the singles (6).
27. Dignitary leaves supporter before race (8).

DOWN

1. Agent is in favour of including the turn (6).
2. Ride in vehicle holding ten, roughly (6).
3. Eggs used for a change? (6).
4. Animals dear to the French, for hunting, perhaps (3-7).
6. Dismissed just for being unqualified? (8).
7. Uphold chief anti-reformer (8).
8. Denounce former era, etc., in assembly (8).
13. Not moving the animals yet? (5-5).
15. Meeting of hands to welcome speaker? (8).
16. Writer appears to run away from girl (8).
17. Corresponding about wash? something upsetting in that (8).
19. In the party? (2-4).
20. Girl goes to border—that's painful (6).
21. Address is one Mrs Turner gives (6).

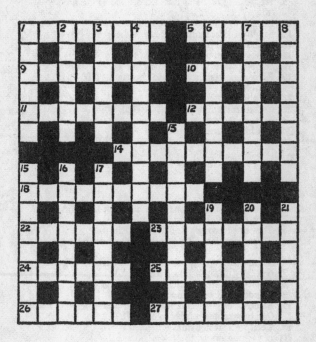

74

ACROSS

1. Appear rash letters, to put it in other words (10).
6. A bit cryptic to a beginner? (6).
9. Happening to be at home, I'd divided the money (8).
10. Citizen in odd hat takes Annie out (8).
11. Exultant Essex opener dealt with breaks (6).
12. Wood and the journalist lodged together (8).
14. Exaggerated, and went red? (8).
16. Wine flowing in this festival? (4-4).
19. Renegade has a scheme for beating sound combine (8).
21. Hit the line? (6).
22. Cad in the team fielding? Right! (8).
23. Brings me in more hackneyed verse (8).
24. Get his figures changed! (6).
25. Is inclined to carry on with child, writing letters (10).

DOWN

1. Lamentation from one in a factory (6).
2. Drops a sound rule (4).
3. Choose the wrong reel for the fish (8).
4. Writer gives Dr Guy Parkin £500—I distribute it (7, 7).
5. Some actions in ceremony appear genuine (7).
7. Get on without a bit of trouble (6).
8. He pursued the criminal in the Strand (8, 6).
13. Dunderhead takes too much port (5).
15. Bemused voter loads metal in Devon (8).
17. Oar breaks into pieces in lake (7).
18. Keen to beat net smasher (6).
20. It's wrong about the taxes! (6).
22. Poor Annie's content with port (4).

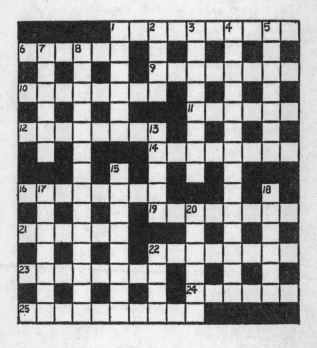

ALPHABETICAL JIGSAW

A   is a person of Bray that's not moved—by a pact about slavery (8).

B   —does he show disbelief? Rather readiness, kindness, and bravery (3, 5).

C   is, I fancy, an integral part—it's what makes a rose ruddy (6).

D   for the resident folk: is religion around after study? (8).

E   is a creature of habit: I don't seem too sure of my title (6).

F   is for deer at the Cape: in the passage there's energy vital (8).

G   the return of a lark to the country's for ornaments floral (8).

H   will betoken approval: repeat your activity aural (4, 4).

I   is round church when Mass starts, where auroral intensity's equal (9).

J   makes one jealous in Germany: yes, and cold comfort's the sequel (8).

K   say our task isn't complex, to keep the command categorical (8).

L   round a loch is for bread, or applied to a lump metaphorical (6).

M   said the V—and I quote—this when George came in P time occurred, sir (8, 3, 6, 3, 3).

N   a wrong-headed magician, he wasn't with William the Third, sir (3-5).

O   start at speed to perform a theatrical (maybe) proceeding (7).

P   is a dog round a river, upset: you can prove it by feeding (7).

Q   nearly twenty-four sheets in a pound—hill, or palace that's Roman (8).

R   is a rake on a pole: Joan of Arc here was burnt by her foemen (5).

S   is an agent that goes without sleep: make it speedy or brittle (6).

T   holds the views of Aquinas with haze, although previously little (7).

U   will turn up with a nurse to give money: your lips you must straighten (7).

V   is a transport that's numbered, whose job is to battle with Satan (5).

W   slogans or whoops: for atrocities, enter a figure (3-5).

X   a ten-page dissertation? That's tiny: a proton is bigger (1-8).

Y   isn't quite a half-volley: it's new in American humour (6).

Z   Round the tavern my auntie from Italy's making a bloomer (6).

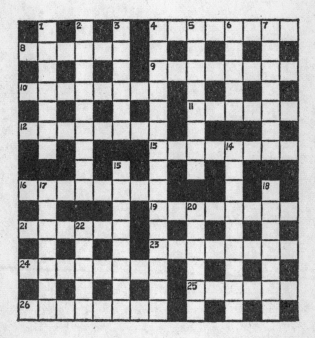

SOLUTIONS

1

ACROSS

1 French Polish; 8 Omicron; 9 Car Wash; 11 Station; 12 Richest; 13 Riser; 14 Caballero; 16 Auricular; 19 Scrip; 21 Inverts; 23 Easeful; 24 Eremite; 25 Oversee; 26 Saul of Tarsus.

DOWN

1 Fridays; 2 Earlier; 3 Canonical; 4 Pacer; 5 Lyrical; 6 Scalene; 7 Conservative; 10 Hot Gospeller; 15 Barcelona; 17 Riviera; 18 Cordial; 19 Sisters; 20 Refuses; 22 Sheaf.

2

ACROSS

8 Talisman; 9 Hooker; 10 Studio; 11 Immodest; 12 Solo; 13 Tiger-Shark; 15 Hopping; 16 Scamper; 18 Hearts-Ease; 19 Elan; 20 Studious; 22 Toledo; 23 Edison; 24 Emotions.

DOWN

1 Bartholomew-Tide; 2 Birds of Paradise; 3 Importunes; 4 Innings; 5 Sham; 6 Lord Chamberlain; 7 Lesser Celandine; 14 Recreation; 17 Tapster; 21 Owns.

3

1 Performance; 8 Apse; 10 Tennis-Ball; 11 Solo; 14 Nurse; 15 Remiss; 17 Delays; 19 Moonlight-Sonata; 20 Noting; 22 Fender; 23 Avail; 24 Tang; 27 Indian Club; 28 Oder; 29 Star Chamber.

DOWN

2 Etty; 3 Fund; 4 Reigns; 5 Albert Chevalier; 6 Called; 7 Below Stairs; 9 Propaganda; 12 Premonition; 13 Importance; 16 Salon; 18 Erode; 21 Gannet; 22 Flinch; 25 Plum; 26 Able.

4

ACROSS

4 Taffrail; 8 Handle; 9 Mantilla; 10 Making Up; 11 Brevet; 12 Listener; 13 Airiness; 16 Magnetic; 19 Elevator; 21 Common; 23 Overhead; 24 Signpost; 25 Pamela; 26 Shadwell.

DOWN

1 Samaria; 2 Addiction; 3 Bergen; 4 Temperance Hotel; 5 Finsbury; 6 Raise; 7 Illness; 14 Not at Home; 15 Stanhope; 17 Abolish; 18 Potable; 20 Exempt; 22 Monad.

5

ACROSS

1 Peter Alliss; 8 Igor; 10 Pitching In; 11 Plum;
14 Midge; 15, 17 George Duncan; 19 Length of the
Putt; 20 Tongas; 22 Pauser; 23 In All; 24 Riot;
27 As they come; 28 Acts; 29 Walter Hagen.

DOWN

2 Espy; 3 Etty; 4 At Home; 5 Lined up for the
Shot; 6 Sliced; 7 Premonitory; 9 Golf Course; 12
Egalitarian; 13 Down-and-out; 16 Gutta; 18
Ulema; 21 Siesta; 22 Player; 25 Iota; 26 Mere.

6

ACROSS

1 Arabia; 5 Regicide; 9, 10, 23 Thousand and One
Nights; 11 Scheherezade; 13 Cadi; 14 Tea-Party;
17 Gymkhana; 18 See 22; 20 A Hundred Days;
23 See 9; 24 Loophole 25 Issuance; 26 Nudity.

DOWN

2 Ruhr; 3 Brunswick; 4 Apathy; 5 Red, White and
Blue; 6 Go Abroad; 7 Cadiz; 8 Denudation; 12
Easy-Chairs; 15 See 19; 16 Harrison; 19 and 15
Haroun Alraschid; 21 Nehru; 22, 18 Flat Roof.

7

ACROSS

1 Stop-Cock; 5 Vassal; 9 Infamous; 10 Colour;
12 Hirer; 13 Knife-Edge; 14 Adventitious; 18 But-
tered Eggs; 21 Eumenides; 23 Roman; 24 Vilely;
25 Redolent; 26 Resent; 27 Asphodel.

DOWN

1 Slight; 2 Oxford; 3 Cambridge; 4 Chuckle-Heads;
6 Arose; 7 Snowdrop; 8 Largesse; 11 Listlessness;
15 Tiger-Moth; 16 Observer; 17 Stimulus; 19 Im-
pend; 20 Instil; 22 Nylon.

8

ACROSS

8 Farewell; 9 Yearly; 10 Plea; 11, 12 The Student
Prince; 14 Tortures; 15 Stomach; 17 Raffish; 20
Spinster; 22 Duddon; 23 Flat-Racing; 24 Goth;
25 Drivel; 26 Abundant.

DOWN

1 Ballarat; 2 Vera; 3 Kettle; 4 Alberta; 5 Hysteria;
6 Handcuffed; 7 Glance; 13 Nominative; 16 Cat-
Calls; 18 Scouting; 19 Orbital; 21 Paltry; 22 Dug-
out; 24 Gide.

9

ACROSS

1 The Bar; 5 Tiresome; 9 Sparable; 10 Charge;
11 It is a Promise; 13 Chat; 14 Overlord; 17 Carry
Out; 18 Tate; 20 Actinometers; 23 Escape; 24
Advocate; 25 Idolised; 26 Notary.

DOWN

2 Hope; 3 Barrister; 4 Rabbit; 5 The Law of the
Land; 6 Recorder; 7 Spasm; 8 Magistrate; 12 The
Accused; 15 Latest Cut; 16 Coroners; 19 Leaven;
21 In all; 22 Stir.

10

ACROSS

7 Leopard; 8 Rose-Buck; 10 Ferret; 11 Elk-Hound;
12 Goat; 13 Rock-Rabbit; 14 Prairie-Wolf; 19
Pine-Marten; 22 Vole; 23 Kangaroo; 24 Marmot;
25 Bullock; 26 Lurcher.

DOWN

1 Develop; 2 Operator; 3 Grater; 4 Cock-Crow;
5 Absorb; 6 Scandic; 9 Description; 15 In a Trice;
16 Laverock; 17 Piraeus; 18 Bloomer; 20 Engulf;
21 Nimbus.

11

ACROSS

1 Indianapolis; 8 Antwerp; 9 Lourdes; 11 Gwalior;
12 Patandi; 13 Masse; 14 Gibraltar; 16 Saragossa;
19 Luton; 21 Extends; 23 Detroit; 24 San Remo;
25 Rangoon; 26 Bloemfontein.

DOWN

1 In-Tears; 2 Deeside; 3 Asparagus; 4 All-Up; 5
Opuntia; 6 In-Doubt; 7 Barge-Masters; 10 Stirring
Tune; 15 Brand-Iron; 17 Retinol; 18 Genoese; 19
Latence; 20 Too Soon; 22 Spoof.

12

ACROSS

1 Suppressed; 6 Health; 9 Annalist; 10 Driveway;
11 Lasses; 12 Stripped; 14 Astounds; 16 Bridport;
19 Escaping; 21 Advent; 22 Kangaroo; 23 Aure-
lian; 24 Aeneas; 25 Chesterton.

DOWN

1 Show-Up; 2 Play; 3 Ringlets; 4 Salisbury Plain;
5 East End; 7 Egrets; 8 Love-in-Idleness; 13 Dante;
15 Contrite; 17 Redruth; 18 Angola; 20 Canaan;
22 Knot.

13

ACROSS

1, 5 Had to go Without; 10, 11 Hope for the Best;
12, 13 Border Terriers; 14 Yorkshire; 16 Leven;
17, 19 Sheet Lightning; 23 Crescent; 24 Circus; 26,
27 Attendance Card; 28 Bridget; 29 Estelle.

DOWN

2 Amoroso; 3 Tweed; 4 Go-Forth; 6 Inhere; 7
Hebridean; 8 Upsurge; 9 Pretermitting; 15 Knees
Bend; 18 Heritor; 20 Hackees; 21 Neutral; 22
Needle; 25 Rache.

14

ACROSS

1 Parliamentary; 10 Allegoric; 11 Udder; 12 Ravel;
13 Stamp Book; 14 Travels; 16 Pattern; 18 Alem-
bic; 20 Morocco; 21 Halloween; 23 Split; 24
Opted; 25 Saturnine; 26 Secretary Bird.

DOWN

2 Alleviate; 3 Legal; 4 Arrests; 5 Enclasp; 6 Trum-
peter; 7 Radio; 8 Parrot Fashion; 9 Broken Bottles;
15 Embroider; 17 Excelsior; 19 Cresset; 20
Monitor; 22 Lathe; 23 Scrub.

15

1 Ducks and Drakes; 8 Venom; 9 Obsolete; 11 Lie-Abed; 12 Abstain; 13 Angle; 15 Yorkshire; 17 Cease Fire; 20 Sheer; 21 Redraft; 23 Friable; 25 Dragoman; 26 Irish; 27 Expressionless.

DOWN

1 Devil-May-Care; 2 Canoe; 3 Semibreve; 4 Noonday; 5 Despair; 6 Arles; 7 Extradite; 10 Knee Breeches; 14 Grand Prix; 16 Suspicion; 18 Isthmus; 19 Effendi; 22 Auger; 24 Beige.

16

ACROSS

1 George the Fourth; 8 Taffrail; 9 Bedbug; 10 Normandy; 11 Uphill; 13 Compassion; 16 Elasticity; 19 Hoop-la; 20 Hot Water; 21 Uniats; 22 Caligari; 23 Earl of Rochester.

DOWN

1, 2 Get on Like a House on Fire; 3 German; 4 Third-Force; 5 Overpass; 6 Rabbinic; 7 Highland Terrier; 12 Apotropaic; 14 Sabotier; 15 Stiletto; 17 Awhile; 18 Strait.

17

DOWN

1 Archbishoprics; 9 Fondlings; 10 Bantu; 11 Clear;
12 Longshore; 13 Innovate; 14 Istria; 17 Nectar;
19 Talisman; 22 Turnstone; 24 Noses; 25 Label; 26
Cake Knife; 27 Never-Never Land.

ACROSS

1 Affectionately; 2 Canteen; 3 Belgravia; 4 Senility;
5 Orsino; 6 Rebus; 7 Candour; 8 Queen Anne's
Dead; 15 Spinnaker; 16 Malenkov; 18 Currble; 20
Messina; 21 Toucan; 23 Solve.

18

ACROSS

1 Simpers; 5 Palaver; 9 Tonga; 10 Airedales; 11
Franciscan; 12 Once; 14 Patron Saint; 18 Counten-
ance; 21 Asps; 22 Protestant; 25 Partridge; 26
Olive; 27 Disease; 29 Dissent.

DOWN

1 Set Off; 2 Monday; 3 Emancipate; 4 Seams; 5
Portadown; 6 Lode; 7 Valencia; 8 Respects; 13
Aspersions; 15 Tonbridge; 16 Scrapped; 17 Sup-
ports; 19 Valise; 20 Attest; 23 Tweed; 24 Area.

ACROSS

7 Droop; 8 Cornelian; 9 First; 10 Behaviour; 12 Accountable; 16 Skit; 17 Sound; 18 Elan; 19 Categorical; 22 Utterance; 24 Lemon; 25 Formality; 26 Leant.

DOWN

1 Fruit Cake; 2 Boy Scouts; 3 Core; 4 Uncabled-For; 5 Plain; 6 Value; 11 Inescapable; 13 Acute; 14 Perimeter; 15 Paramount; 20 Stool; 21 Seamy; 23 City.

20

ACROSS

8 Eldritch; 9 Captor; 10 Purser; 11 Sobriety; 12 Pert; 13 Half-Crowns; 15 Attempt; 16 Gun-Boat; 18 Ground Rent; 19 Urdu; 20 Shrivels; 22 Theory; 23 Armour; 24 Dewberry.

DOWN

1 Gloucestershire; 2 Cross the Rubicon; 3 Star-Shaped; 4 Thistle; 5 Seab; 6 A Pair of Blue Eyes; 7 Bolton Wanderers; 14 County Town; 17 Seaside; 21 Eyre.

21

ACROSS

1 Ilkley Moor; 8 Echo; 10 Festooning; 11 Hook;
13 Pasties; 15 Brazen; 16 Russia; 17 We Get Our
Own Back; 18 Ingrid; 20 Placid; 21 No Entry; 22
Duck; 25 Enchanting; 26 Worm; 27 Sisterless.

DOWN

2, 3 Lifeless; 4 Yeoman; 5 Ornithorhynchus; 6
Runner; 7 Pockmarked; 9 Cross-Patch; 12
Baggage-Car; 13 Pertain; 14 Sunnily; 15 Bow-
Windows; 19 Doings; 20 Prince; 23 Bill; 24 Eggs.

22

ACROSS

1 Dabchick; 5 Scrawl; 9 Resident; 10 Paling; 11
Home Department; 14 Hands; 15 Datum; 16
Heard; 17 Sides; 20 Licit; 22 Draw the Long Bow;
24 Ironed; 25 Delaware; 26 Ernest; 27 Psalters.

DOWN

1 Dore; 2 Bassoon; 3 Hedgers; 4 Consequence; 6
Chatted; 7 Aliment; 8 Legitimate; 12 Astronomers;
13 Whist-Drive; 18 Dragoon; 19 Setters; 20 Leg-
Bail; 21 Chorale; 23 Pets.

23

ACROSS

8 Whistler; 9 Exeunt; 10 Renata; 11 Act of God;
12 Peri; 13 Pro-marxist; 15 Section; 16 Tool-Kit;
18 Steerforth; 19 Noun; 20 Thronged; 22 Rating;
23 Pursed; 24 Contrast.

DOWN

1 The Eleventh Hour; 2 A Seat in the House; 3
Clear Proof; 4 Treason; 5 Pent; 6 Self-Explana-
tory; 7 Unconsciousness; 14 Another-One; 17 Pre-
dict; 21 Gide.

24

ACROSS

1 Disappointment; 9 Sheerness; 10 Youth; 11 Extra;
12 Plaintiff; 13 Teetotum; 14 Washer; 17 Esmond;
19 Cataract; 22 Venetians; 24 Taste; 25 Corgi; 26
Trombones; 27 The First Person.

DOWN

1 Dessert-Service; 2 Sheltie; 3 Portadown; 4 Over-
plus; 5 Nassau; 6 Mayan; 7 Nourish; 8 The First
Lesson; 15 Adaptable; 16 Passport; 18 Monarch;
20 Assents; 21 Matter; 23 Thief.

25

ACROSS

1 Beside-Oneself; 8 The Odyssey; 9 Kiev; 11 Achilles; 12 Milton; 14 Denis; 15 Harsh; 16 Tense; 17 Equal; 20 Biter; 22 Toyish; 23 Theodicy; 25 Huss; 26 Spermaceti; 27 Scotch-Thistle.

DOWN

1 Bath and West Show; 2, 3 Stephen Dedalus; 4 Oyster-Beds; 5 Eden; 6 Fritter; 7 Seven Thirty-Nine; 10 Fish; 13 Disinherit; 18 Ulysses; 19 Loss; 20 Bhowani; 21 Trident; 24 Epic.

26

ACROSS

8 Converse; 9 Sterne; 10 Pawnee; 11 Moorcock; 12 Alph; 13 Tender-Loin; 15 Platoon; 16 Lighter; 18 Incredible; 19 Reef; 20 Estimate; 22 Twelve; 23 Angler; 24 Sea-Perch.

DOWN

1 For Auld Lang Syne; 2 Ivan the Terrible; 3 Priesthood; 4 Germane; 5 Oslo; 6 Pencil-Sharpener; 7 On Active Service; 14 Evidential; 17 Abreast; 21 Agra.

27

ACROSS

1 Billingham; 8 Gate; 10 Spennymoor; 11 Fact; 13 Otaries; 15, 18 County Durham; 16 Dorsal; 17 Radiotelegraphy; 18 See 15. 20 Antler; 21 Nagging; 22 Alas; 25 Hartlepool; 26 Eddy; 27 Darlington.

DOWN

2 Ipso; 3 Lied; 4 Ninety; 5 Homeric Laughter; 6 Mooted; 7 Test-Player; 9 Adams Apple; 12 Sunderland; 13 Ottoman; 14 Soaring; 15 Corn-Dealer; 19 Maraud; 20 Angeli; 23 Song; 24 Alto.

ACROSS

1 Trouble In Store; 9 Enteron; 10 Wantage; 11 Elias; 12 Blue Skies; 13 Servilely; 14, 6 Sugar-Tongs; 15 Ensue; 17 Wokingham; 20 D'Artagnan; 22 Harem; 23 Notices; 24 Lardoon; 25 Forth-rightness.

DOWN

1 The Bees Wedding; 2 Outlier; 3 Berkshire; 4 Ennoble; 5 Newbury; 6 See 14 Across; 7 Reading; 8 Leisure Moments; 14 Sandhurst; 16 Stretto; 17 Windsor; 18 King Log; 19 Hormone; 21 Ascot.

29

ACROSS

1 Spalding; 5 Status; 9 Stamford; 10 Bureau; 11 Point of Contact; 14 Agent; 15 Yahoo; 16 See 19; 17 Vigil; 20 Aesop; 22 Science Fiction; 24 Boston; 25 Skegness; 26 Guyana; 27 Sleaford.

DOWN

1 Sash; 2 A la Mode; 3 Defunct; 4 Narrow-Shave; 6 Tourney; 7 The Wash; 8 Scunthorpe; 12 Cupro-Nickel; 13 Harvest-Bug; 18 Grimsby; 19, 16 Lincolnshire; 20 Antigua; Spoleto; 23 Used.

30

ACROSS

8 Yokohama; 9 Nelson; 10 Eton; 11 Stonehaven; 12 Calais; 14 Eversley; 15 Bewdley; 17 St Neots; 20 Pretoria; 22 Naples; 23 New Orleans; 24 Deal; 25 Bedale; 26 Aberdeen.

DOWN

1 Foot-Page; 2 Town; 3 Lasses; 4 Damosel; 5 Interest; 6 Clean Sweep; 7 Cohere; 13 Additional; 16 Enrolled; 18 The Dales; 19 Caravan; 21 Reeled; 22 Nested; 24 Dido.

31

7 Aynho; 8 Thrapston; 9 See 11; 10 Kettering, 12 Allegorises; 16 Ogre; 17 Tress; 18 Ants; 19 Earls Barton; 22 Decompose; 24 Corby; 25 Text-Books; 26 Bible.

DOWN

1 Mythology; 2 Shortened; 3 Shoe; 4 Castle-Ashby; 5 Usurp; 6 Bound; 11, 9 Northamptonshire; 13 Ideal; 14 Patriotic; 15 Stoolball; 20 Peter; 21 North; 23 Soke.

32

ACROSS

1 Cumberland; 6 Aurora; 9 Rapacity; 10 Friendly; 11 Sentry; 12 Aspatria; 14 Carlisle; 16 Egremont; 19 Egoistic; 21 Rag-Tag; 22 Permeate; 23 Dove Sono; 24 Essene; 25 Workington.

DOWN

1 Calder; 2, 22 Maryport; 3 Exposure; 4 Licentiousness; 5 Natural; 7 Unrest; 8 One Day Next Week; 13 Acute; 15 Longtown; 17 Giacomo; 18 Wigton; 20 O'Brien; 22 See 2.

33

ACROSS

7 River; 8 Tennessee; 9 Adige; 10 Euphrates; 12 Watercourse; 16 Menu; 17 Loire; 18 Eden; 19 Brahmaputra; 22 Great Fish; 24 Annan; 25 Estuaries; 26 Onega.

DOWN

1 Findlater; 2 Weighed Up; 3 Peru; 4 On the Seesaw; 5 Assam; 6 Weser; 11 Scalpriform; 13 Uriah; 14 Repugnant; 15 Rearrange; 20 Dress; 21 Tagus; 23 Spey.

34

ACROSS

1 John Galsworthy; 8 Genii; 9 Redivide; 11 Austere; 12 Warpath; 13 Put Up; 15 Scribbler; 17 Zeitgeist; 20 Tacky; 21 Lion Cub; 23 Pleader; 25 Hillside; 26 Cabin; 27 A Man of Property.

DOWN

1 Jigsaw Puzzle; 2 Hunts; 3 Guinea-Pig; 4 Largess; 5 Widower; 6 River; 7 Hydraulic; 10 Cherry Brandy; 14 Triforium; 16 Buttercup; 18 In Brief; 19 Top Gear; 22 Colon; 24 Debar.

35

ACROSS

8 Baseball; 9 Hockey; 10 Snap; 11 Recreation; 12 Soccer; 14 Instance; 15 Cricket; 17 Slogger; 20 Lacrosse; 22 Seesaw; 23 Roundabout; 24 Golf; 25 Crease; 26 Sculling.

DOWN

1 Barn-Door; 2 Leap; 3 Fairer; 4 Flaccid; 5 The Easel; 6 Acute Angle; 7 Heroic; 13 Ciceronian; 16 Enslaved; 18 Enabling; 19 Remorse; 21 Aboard; 22 Set Out; 24 Gull.

36

ACROSS

8 Threaten; 9 Heated; 10 Wheeze; 11 Lacrosse; 12 Buss; 13 Devonshire; 15 Rebound; 16 Atavism; 18 Off the Cuff; 19 Nest; 20 Isotonic; 22 Anyway; 23 Temper; 24 Mill-Race.

DOWN

1 The House of Usher; 2 Reversion to Type; 3 Attendance; 4 Enslave; 5 Chic; 6 Naboth's Vineyard; 7 Least Resistance; 14 Notifiable; 17 Outcome; 21 Norm.

37

ACROSS

8 Somerset; 9 Stairs; 10 Oder; 11 Earlestown; 12 Sought; 14 Hebrides; 15 Addenda; 17 Bengali; 20 Abundant; 22 Missal; 23 More or Less; 24 Ache; 25 Scarab; 26 Chileans.

DOWN

1 Goodwood; 2 Gear; 3 Assert; 4 Starchy; 5 Assemble; 6 Partridges; 7 Browse; 13 Green-Heart; 16 Diatribe; 18 Loathing; 19 Stretch; 21 Broach; 22 Mashie; 24 Area.

38

ACROSS

9, 10, 21 across. The Battle of the Bulge; 11 Antwerp; 12 Ignored; 13 Arris; 14 The Allies; 16 European Theatre; 19 Suggested; 21 See 9; 22 Haricot; 23 The Bomb; 24 Adage; 25 Rundstedt.

DOWN

1 Stratagems; 2 Venturer; 3 Gapers; 4 Stop; 5 Regimented; 6 Down-Club; 7 Iturbi; 8 Vend; 14 Tractators; 15 Stereobate; 17 Preacher; 18 Tallowed; 20 German; 21 Breast; 22, 23 Heartens.

39

ACROSS

4 Official; 8 Canape; 9 Erastian; 10 Lothario; 11 Inside; 12 Parlance; 13 Regiment; 16 Crayfish; 19 Eligible; 21 Ascent; 23 Intruder; 24 Sing-Sing; 25 Menace; 26 Aegrotat.

DOWN

1 Samovar; 2 Pathology; 3 Hebron; 4 One-Over-The-Eight; 5 Flamingo; 6 Cutis; 7 Abandon; 14 Marijuana; 15 District; 17 Respite; 18 Fluency; 20 In Time; 22 Eager.

ACROSS

1 Concentration; 8 Unemployed; 9 Gray; 11 Iolanthe; 12 Dorado; 14 Nashe; 15 Plain; 16 Psalm; 17 Ripon; 20 Dupin; 22 Tenets; 23 Ink-Wells; 25 Leer; 26 Pastmaster; 27 Sergeants' Mess.

DOWN

1 Cautionary Tales; 2 Needles; 3 Expanse; 4 Tooth-Paste; 5 Aver; 6 Nirvana; 7 Lay Down Ones Arms; 10 Soup; 13 Wellington; 18 Punters; 19 Note; 20 Dewlaps; 21 Palette; 24 Case.

41

ACROSS

1 Aphrodisiac; 8 Idle; 10 Candelabra; 11 Pace; 14 Nudge; 15 Farina; 17 Dry-Bob; 19 Infantry-Soldier; 20 Morose; 22 Bright; 23 Curse; 24 Them; 27 Laceration; 28 Vote; 29 Crestfallen.

DOWN

2 Puck; 3 Runt; 4 Duenna; 5 Stand by Your Beds; 6 Agreed; 7 Reverberate; 9 Drawbridge; 12 Affirmative; 13 Preferment; 16 Nines; 18 Ruler; 21 Eclair; 22 Behalf; 25 Girl; 26 Once.

42

ACROSS

1, 5 Flying Dutchman; 9 Disproof; 10 Indigo; 11 Dessert-Spoon; 13 See 2; 14 Eyesight; 17 Utterest; 18, 22 Moby Dick; 20 Faint-Hearted; 23 Stolen; 24 Isobaric; 25 Grandson; 26 Greeks.

DOWN

2, 13 Laid-Down; 3 Impudence; 4 Glossy; 5 Differentiation; 6 Thirteen; 7 Had Up; 8 Anglophobe; 12 Contractor; 15 Immediate; 16 Methinks; 19 Strong; 21 Nylon; 22 See 18.

43

ACROSS

1 Backwash; 5 Shadow; 9 Arranged; 10 Unison; 11 Complain; 12 Israel; 14 Agreements; 18 Brilliance; 22 Rental; 23 Antelope; 24 Euclid; 25 Filament; 26 Eleven; 27 Repeater.

DOWN

1 Branch; 2 Chrome; 3 Wangle; 4 Sheringham; 6 Handsome; 7 Disdains; 8 Windlass; 13 Mercantile; 15 Abergele; 16 Binnacle; 17 Flea-Bite; 19 Hecate; 20 Molest; 21 Letter.

44

ACROSS

1, 5 Victoria Albert; 9 Short-Leg; 10 Museum; 11 Oaklings; 12 Stater; 14 Watch-Chain; 18 Second-Hand; 22 London; 23 Capitals; 24 Throne; 25 Time-Fuse; 26 Drones; 27 Pendulum.

DOWN

1 Vision; 2 Clocks; 3 Obtain; 4 Ideographs; 6 Loud Tick; 7 Eventual; 8 Tamarind; 13 Scandalise; 15 Isolated; 16 Scenario; 17 Announce; 19 Gilead; 20 Casual; 21 Esteem.

45

ACROSS

1 Correspondences; 8 Rightist; 9 Redeem; 10 Marginal; 11 Gretna; 13 Kenilworth; 16 Overpraise; 19 Shaman; 20 Elliptic; 21 Erotic; 22 Keelhaul; 23 Substitutionary.

DOWN

1 Ceremoniousness; 2 Regard; 3 Entail; 4 Passageway; 5 Eyebrows; 6 Creature; 7 Sympathetically; 12 Dissolvent; 14 Hecatomb; 15 Apiarist; 17 Rialto; 18 Ithaca.

46

ACROSS

1 Come to Hand; 6 Staffa; 9 Sternest; 10 Triolets; 11 Priors; 12 Sorbonne; 14 Meal-Time; 16 Palliate; 19 November; 21 Direct; 22 Palgrave; 23 Pershore; 24 Sparse; 25 Stay-At-Home.

DOWN

1 Cavern; 2 Mass; 3 Thespian; 4 Henrietta Maria; 5 Nostrum; 7 Tarpon; 8 Football-Jersey; 13 Emden; 15 Last Post; 17 Aliment; 18 Leaves; 20 Valise; 22 Peso.

47

ACROSS

1 Factory Farming; 9 Electrode; 10 Super; 11 Extra; 12 Assertion; 13 Tertiary; 14 Amulet; 17 Resume; 19 Terrific; 22 Round Trip; 24 Carol; 25 Safer; 26 Totem Pole; 27 Electric Kettle.

DOWN

1 Free Enterprise; 2 Chester; 3 Ostracise; 4 Yeomanry; 5 Averse; 6 Miser; 7 Nuptial; 8 Trinity College; 15 Morecambe; 16 Despotic; 18 Soulful; 20 Fur Coat; 21 Orator; 23 Doric.

ACROSS

1 Hard-Boiled Eggs; 9 Sibling; 10 Sistine; 11 Aston; 12 Timepiece; 13 Gloss; 15 Rotterdam; 17 Amsterdam; 18 Regan; 19 Libellous; 22 Sheet; 23 Florist; 24 Marengo; 25 Exchequer Bill.

DOWN

2 Ambitious; 3 Deign; 4 Ought; 5 Disappear; 6 Gripe; 7 As Large as Life; 8 Determination; 10 Sympton; 14 Shellfish; 15 Redcoat; 16 Dog-Kennel; 20 Bronx; 21 Somme; 22 Scrub.

49

ACROSS

7 Nails; 8 Night-Wear; 9 Derby; 10 Whitebait;
12 Scarborough; 16 Hint; 17 Pippa; 18 Item; 19
French Chalk; 22 Novelists; 24 Rabat; 25 Messa-
lina; 26 Galen.

DOWN

1 Paper-Clip; 2 Elaborate; 3 Nith; 4 Photographs;
5 Swabs; 6, 11 David Copperfield; 13 Orpen; 14
Right Away; 15 Tea Leaves; 20 Dover; 21 Yeast;
23 Tend.

50

ACROSS

1 My Dear; 5, 26 Sherlock Holmes; 9 Arrogate;
10 Piping; 11 In the Running; 13 Elan; 14 Fraction;
17 Smallish; 18 Tell; 20 On the Decline; 23 Watson;
24 In Houses; 25 Eye-Piece; 26 See 5 Across.

DOWN

2 Yard; 3 Emotional; 4 Realty; 5 Scene of the
Crime; 6 Espousal; 7 Lupin; 8 Conan Doyle; 12,
1, 23 Elementary, My Dear Watson; 15 To the
Full; 16 Riddance; 19 Eighth; 21 Has Up; 22 Bede.

178

51

1 Sophism; 5 Cobbett; 9 Abrim; 10 Guards Van;
11 Radicalism; 12 Alit; 14 Litmus Paper; 18 First
Lesson; 21 Each; 22 Stock-Yards; 25 Acid Drops;
26 Opine; 27 Lunette; 28 Screens.

DOWN

1 Stairs; 2 Parade; 3 Immaculate; 4 Mogue; 5
Chasseurs; 6 Beds; 7 Envelope; 8 Tincture; 13
Spennymoor; 15 Twenty-One; 16 After All; 17
Friction; 19 Ermine; 20 Osiers; 23 Cases; 24 Edit.

52

ACROSS

1 The Life of Riley; 9 Eccentric; 10 Negro; 11
Adage; 12 Selection; 13 Olympiad; 14 Itchen; 17
Lahore; 19 Pivot-Gun; 22 Xylophone; 24 Hates; 25
Rabbi; 26 Impromptu; 27 Stumbling Block.

DOWN

1 The Lap of Luxury; 2 Encraty; 3 Inn-Keeper;
4 Etruscan; 5 Facile; 6 Ionic; 7 English; 8 Down
on ones luck; 15 Tooth-Comb; 16 Fine-Spun; 18
Halibut; 20 Get Up To; 21 Jovial; 23 Priam.

53

ACROSS

9 Larghetto; 10 Amuse; 11 Inn Sign; 12 Tool-Kit;
13 Crest; 14 Wood-Smoke; 16 Merchant Taylors;
19 Uppingham; 21 Rugby; 22 Alleyns; 23 Topknot;
24 Stowe; 25 Explosive.

DOWN

1 Plaid Cymru; 2 Grandeur; 3 Thrift; 4 Eton; 5
Post Mortem; 6 Famously; 7 Cuckoo; 8 Felt;
14 Winchester; 15 Essayettes; 17 Honey-Bee; 18
Organdie; 20 Pillow; 21 Repton; 22 Also; 23 Type.

54

ACROSS

1, 5 Rudyard-Kipling; 9 Posed; 10 Famous Men;
11 Discovered; 12 Anil; 14 On All Points; 18
Electrotype; 21 Ursa; 22 Kick-Up-a-Row; 25 Noble
Pile; 26 Idiot; 27 Whereon; 28 Sit There.

DOWN

1 Rabids; 2 Desist; 3 And So Forth; 4 Defoe; 5
Kimberley; 6 Plug; 7 Immanent; 8 Gentlest; 13
Cover-Point; 15 Abolition; 16 Let Us Now; 17
Feasible; 19 Praise; 20 Swathe; 23 Keeps; 24 Hebe.

ACROSS

1 Sluggish; 5 Scarab; 9 Lampeter; 10 Darnel; 12 Erect; 13 Tinctures; 14 Accidentally; 18 Capitulation; 21 Vacillate; 23 Brows; 24 Nelson; 25 Poundage; 26 Endues; 27 Pensions.

DOWN

1 Silver; 2 Unmeet; 3 Great Scot; 4 Sweet-William; 6 Chant; 7 Rent-Roll; 8 Bulls-Eye; 11 Under the Rose; 15 Trombones; 16 Scavenge; 17 Speckled; 19 Potato; 20 Aspens; 22 Loose.

ACROSS

1 Netted; 5 Observes; 9 Crossbow; 10 Lister; 11 Extortionate; 13 Apse; 14 Corduroy; 17 Fresh Air; 18 Diet; 20 Giant Despair; 23 Libyan; 24 Initials; 25 Egg-Spoon; 26 Events.

DOWN

2 Earn; 3 Tasteless; 4 Debate; 5, 6 Onward Christian Soldiers; 7 Resin; 8 Electrodes; 12 Appraising; 15 Underline; 16 Fandango; 19 Malice; 21 Noyes; 22 Flat.

57

ACROSS

4 Sympathy; 8 Vermin; 9 Purchase; 10 Floodlit; 11 Insult; 12 Bacteria; 13 Grasmere; 16 Pantheon; 19 Aspirate; 21 Enosis; 23 Immunity; 24 Alhambra; 25 Admire; 26 Progress.

DOWN

1 Bellman; 2 Important; 3 Angler; 4 Septuagenarians; 5 Marginal; 6 Athos; 7 Hustler; 14 Metronome; 15 Feasible; 17 Annular; 18 Stature; 20 Pampas; 22 Slang.

58

ACROSS

1 Intempestive; 8 Nunnery; 9 Airpump; 11 Know-All; 12 Traitor; 13 Caste; 14 Wednesday; 16 Ambergris; 19 Copra; 21 Misword; 23 In Train; 24 Rainbow; 25 Shatter; 26 Electroylsis.

DOWN

1 Igneous; 2 Teenage; 3 Mayflower; 4 Exact; 5 Terrace; 6 Vaulted; 7 Snake-Charmer; 10 Party Manners; 15 Dismissay; 17 Be-Still; 18 Rhombic; 19 Cutlass; 20 Plautus; 22 Dower.

59

ACROSS

8 Latitude; 9 Loiter; 10 Lawn; 11 Latent Heat; 12 Lallan; 14 Lilliput; 15 Lady-Fly; 17 Lingula; 20 Llanabba; 22 Laputa; 23 Lambdacism; 24 Lyre; 25 Legree; 26 L'Allegro.

DOWN

1 Lava-Lava; 2 Lion; 3 Lublin; 4 Lentils; 5 Llanelli; 6 Lighting-Up; 7 Lefanu; 13 Laying Bare; 16 Librated; 18 Literary; 19 Labials; 21 Leaven; 22 Limply; 24 Leek.

60

ACROSS

1 Entrance; 5 Sparse; 9 Gangrene; 10 Toffee; 11 Gorgeous; 12 Strait; 14 Importuned; 18 Laboratory; 22 Arrest; 23 Ecliptic; 24 United; 25 Air-Tight; 26 Events; 27 Increase.

DOWN

1 Engage; 2 Tenure; 3 Agreed; 4 Consummate; 6 Prostate; 7 Refrains, 8 Eventide; 13 Correction; 15 Pleasure; 16 Abortive; 17 Crescent; 19 Winter; 20 Stigma; 21 Scathe.

61

ACROSS

1 See 25; 5 Bondage; 9 Human; 10 Sweet-Shop;
11 Last Season; 12 Anon; 14 Painted Veil; 18
Cakes and Ale; 21 Lass; 22 Razors Edge; 25, 1
Across W. Somerset Maugham; 26 Onset; 27
Guereza; 28 Cleaner.

DOWN

1 Mohole; 2 Unmask; 3 Honest Past; 4 Musca;
5 Brew of Tea; 6 Note; 7 Ashenden; 8 Empanels;
13 Adderstone; 15 Ionian Sea; 16 Scalawag; 17
Ski-Slope; 19 Edison; 20 Setter; 23 Optic; 24 Fete.

62

ACROSS

8 Reindeer; 9 Phonic; 10 Allege; 11 Sinister; 12
Swan; 13 Priesthood; 15 Probity; 16 College; 18
Avouchment; 19 Bred; 20 Elements; 22 To Date;
23 Repose; 24 Sore Eyes.

DOWN

1 Fellow Traveller; 2 Once in a Blue Moon; 3 Fever
Pitch; 4 Crispin; 5 Span; 6 Household Budget; 7
Lives of Great Men; 14 Short Story; 17 Persist;
21 Need.

63

ACROSS

9 Overdrive; 10 Igloo; 11 Tacitus; 12 Redoubt;
13 Naiad; 14 Bridewell; 16 Open and Shut Case;
19 Sandbanks; 21 Holst; 22 Andorra; 23 Shannon;
24 Pasha; 25 Egression.

DOWN

1 Portentous; 2 Perceive; 3 Edited; 4 Miss; 5 Rear
Lights; 6 Wild-West; 7 Clause; 8 Port; 14 Baden-
Baden; 15 Lieutenant; 17 Arboreal; 18 Atlantis;
20 Nudist; 21 Hearse; 22 Alps; 23 Sore.

ACROSS

1 London Transport; 8 Visitors; 9 Inhere; 10 Red-
Faced; 11 Guardi; 13 Tantony Pig; 16 Land
League; 19 Thelma; 20 Shouting; 21 Esteem; 22
Confetti; 23 The Queen's Speech.

DOWN

1 Liverpool Street; 2 No-Side; 3 Outlay; 4 Turned
Away; 5 Sanguine; 6 Overripe; 7 The King's
English; 12 Struthious; 14 Unsettle; 15 Flambeau;
17 Puff Up; 18 Big Toe.

65

ACROSS

1 Rugby League; 8 Oboe; 10 Salfordian; 11 Unit; 14 Enrol; 15 Entail; 17 Elisha; 19 The Second-Row Man; 20 Easter; 22 Vernon; 23 Abele; 24 Odds; 27 Statute Law; 28 Ride; 29 Petrologist.

DOWN

2 Ursa; 3 Ball; 4 Lionel; 5 Anderson Shelter; 6 Unable; 7 Restraining; 9 Banishment; 12 Centre Court; 13 Steep-Sided; 16 Irene; 18 Loose; 21 Rattle; 22 Vestal; 25 Flag; 26 Owes.

66

ACROSS

4 Traffics; 8 Upshot; 9 Envelope; 10 Snowdrop; 11 Wonder; 12 Torridge; 13 Scottish; 16 Cardigan; 19 Turn Down; 21 Stocks; 23 Estimate; 24 Rigadoon; 25 Earned; 26 Sentence.

DOWN

1 Opinion; 2 Shewbread; 3 Stared; 4 The Present Tense; 5 Advowson; 6 Felon; 7 Coppers; 14 Trade Mark; 15 Egg Spoon; 17 Astride; 18 Swathes; 20 Rather; 22 Craft.

67

ACROSS

8 Sergeant; 9 Animal; 10 Fare; 11 Malefactor; 12 Placid; 14 Tribunal; 15 Commute; 17 Measure; 20 Spelling; 22 Midden; 23 Terminates; 24 Pest; 25 Kernel; 26 Thespian.

DOWN

1 Seraglio; 2 Ague; 3 Talmud; 4 Athlete; 5 Caffeine; 6 Discoursed; 7 Pagoda; 13 Complement; 16 Triangle; 18 Rheostat; 19 Agitate; 21 Peeler; 22 Master; 24 Pipe.

ACROSS

8 Simulate; 9 Yo-Ho-Ho; 10 Agatha; 11 Runagate; 12 If So; 13 Tumble-Down; 15 Faintly; 16 Dragoon; 18 Ramshackle; 19 Orts; 20 Hair-Cord; 22 Innate; 23 Fiddle; 24 Antelope.

DOWN

1 King of Barataria; 2 Bunthornes Bride; 3 Tarantella; 4 Begrime; 5 Hymn; 6 The Gods Grown Old; 7 The Town of Titipu; 14 Larcenists; 17 Skiddaw; 21 Owed.

69

ACROSS

8 Guardian; 9 Stewed; 10 Isle; 11 Editorials; 12 Digest; 14 Intimate; 15 Instant; 17 Advance; 20 Detritus; 22 Sterne; 23 Apparition; 24 Mien; 25 Cannon; 26 Extracts.

DOWN

1 Question; 2 Free; 3 Divert; 4 Insipid; 5 Escorted; 6 Medium Rare; 7 Pellet; 13 Entertains; 16 Nutrient; 18 Converts; 19 Aspired; 21 Espial; 22 Senate; 24 Mean.

70

ACROSS

8, 9 Cardinal-Points; 10 Mean; 11 Antithesis; 12 Ballad; 14 Examiner; 15 Placard; 17 Chancel; 20 Starling; 22 Relate; 23 Flamingoes; 24 Tick; 25 Season; 26 Ladybird.

DOWN

1 Baseball; 2 Aden; 3 On Hand; 4 Clatter; 5 Spot Cash; 6 Time-Signal; 7 Stripe; 13 Lachrymose; 16 Reigning; 18 Enticers; 19 Ignoble; 21 Tiller; 22 Reside; 24 Tuba.

71

ACROSS

9 Eliminate; 10 Aroma; 11 Depress; 12 Earnest;
13 Roam; 14 Folkestone; 16 Onerous; 17 Tripoli;
19 Negotiable; 22 Edit; 24 Tangram; 25 Retinue;
26 Alert; 27 Spaghetti.

DOWN

1 Tenderloin Steak; 2 Displace; 3 Wives; 4 Man-
sions; 5 Bedeck; 6 Patristic; 7 Toledo; 8 Castles In
the Air; 15 Posterity; 17 Toll Road; 18 Ordinate;
20 Gannet; 21 Almost; 23 Itchy.

ACROSS

1 Clamped; 5 Stencil; 9 Untie; 10 Tragedian; 11
Nurseryman; 12 Maim; 14 Acumination; 18
Candle-Light; 21 Ruth; 22 Off-Licence; 25 Flower-
ing; 26 Libra; 27 Lasting; 28 Largely.

DOWN

1 Churns; 2 Attire; 3 Preferably; 4 Dotty; 5 Sea-
faring; 6 Eyes; 7 Climatic; 8 Land-Mine; 13 Par-
ticular; 15 Uplifting; 16 Scornful; 17 Unctuous;
19 Unable; 20 Legacy; 23 Legal; 24 Peri.

73

ACROSS

1 Face-Card; 5 Dormie; 9 Conducts; 10 Stripe; 11 Overcoat; 12 Sitter; 14 Scotch Mist; 18 Preference; 22 Leeway; 23 As It Were; 24 Utopia; 25 Kilogram; 26 Eleven; 27 Alderman.

DOWN

1 Factor; 2 Canter; 3 Clutch; 4 Rat-Catcher; 6 Outright; 7 Maintain; 8 Execrate; 13 Stock-Still; 15 Applause; 16 Penelope; 17 Relative; 19 At-Home; 20 Megrim; 21 Sermon.

74

ACROSS

1 Paraphrase; 6 Morsel; 9 Incident; 10 Athenian; 11 Elated; 12 Billeted; 14 Overdrew; 16 Hock-Tide; 19 Rataplan; 21 Stroke; 22 Outsider; 23 Trimeter; 24 Eights; 25 Consonants.

DOWN

1 Plaint; 2 Rain; 3 Pickerel; 4 Rudyard Kipling; 5 Sincere; 7 Obtain; 8 Sherlock Holmes; 13 Dover; 15 Tiverton; 17 Ontario; 18 Lament; 20 Tithes; 22 Oran.

75

ALPHABETICAL JIGSAW

A Assiento; B Boy Scout; C Cyanin; D Denizens; E Ermine; F Foreland; G Garlands; H Hear Hear; I Isochasms; J Jaundice; K Kantists; L Leaven; M Moderate Men Looked Big Sir; N Non Juror; O Operate; P Pudding; Q Quirinal; R Rouen; S Snappy; T Thomist; U Unpurse; V Vicar; W War-Cries; X X-Particle; Y Yorker; Z Zinnia.

RAY REARDON

CLASSIC SNOOKER

Snooker HAS to be fun, says Ray Reardon, six times
World Champion and star of television's 'Pot Black'.
CLASSIC SNOOKER will enable both beginners and
more experienced players to get the maximum enjoyment from this ever-popular sport. Packed with the sort
of practical advice only a first-class player can give,
CLASSIC SNOOKER also reveals how Ray Reardon
played his way to the top.

Fully illustrated with over 150 line drawings, CLASSIC
SNOOKER covers: Basic skills—the grip, the stance,
bridging, striking—Potting—Playing with side—Stop,
stun and screw shots—Positional play—Safety and escape play—Red-black play—Splitting the pack.

CORONET BOOKS

SPORTS AND HOBBIES FROM CORONET

All these books are available at your local bookshop or newsagent, or can be ordered direct from the publisher. Just tick the titles you want and fill in the form below.

Prices and availability subject to change without notice.

....

CORONET BOOKS, P.O. Box 11, Falmouth, Cornwall.

Please send cheque or postal order, and allow the following for postage and packing:

U.K. – One book 25p plus 10p per copy for each additional book ordered, up to a maximum of £1.05.

B.F.P.O. and EIRE – 25p for the first book plus 10p per copy for the next 8 books, thereafter 5p per book.

OTHER OVERSEAS CUSTOMERS – 40p for the first book and 12p per copy for each additional book.

Name...

Address...

....